Ruth Guilding

MARBLE MANIA

SCULPTURE GALLERIES IN ENGLAND
1640–1840

The Soane Gallery

2001

Published in Great Britain 2001
by Sir John Soane's Museum
Reg. Charity No.313609

ISBN 0 9537512 7 9

Supported by the Resource/DCMS
Designation Challenge Fund

Designed and typeset in Albertina by Libanus Press, Marlborough
Printed by BAS Printers Limited, Over Wallop

Title page
Charles Townley's House at Park Street, The Entrance Hall, 1794 (Cat.71)
(The British Museum, London)

Preface

An exhibition on the subject of Sculpture Galleries is a particularly appropriate one for the Museum as many of Soane's works of art come from these early collections and the names of the Earl of Egremont, Lord Burlington, Robert Adam and others evoke memorable associations in Soane's own *Description* of his House and Museum. The exhibition is also of interest to anyone interested in the evolution of museums and galleries as well as to creative artists today who are increasingly inspired by the more personal and imaginative displays of earlier periods.

We have been able to assemble many important works of art to illustrate the subject of 'marble mania' and I am especially grateful to all the lenders who have made this possible. Many thanks also go to the following who have all helped in different ways: Elizabeth Angelicoussis; Dr Malcolm Baker; Dr John Bold; Jane Bush; Michael Daley; Christopher Date; Peter Day; Dr Ruth Harman; Dr Eileen Harris; Charles Hind; Christine Hiskey; Steven Hobbs; Dr Ian Jenkins; John Kenworthy-Browne; Anthony Kersting; Tim Knox; Charles Noble; Mark Norman; Susan Palmer; Dr Christopher Ridgway; Dr John Martin Robinson; Margaret Schuelein; Jonathan Scott; Jonathan Clark of Sotheran's, Piccadilly; David Sturdy; Dr Michael Vickers; Dr David Watkin; Professor John Wilton-Ely and Christopher Woodward. We are also most grateful to the Designation Challenge Fund for supporting the exhibition.

Finally I want to extend especial thanks to Will Palin, our Assistant Curator, for organising the exhibition and to Dr Ruth Guilding, our guest curator, to whom we owe the idea of presenting this subject in the first place and who has successfully assembled so many key works of art as well as writing a wonderful catalogue.

MARGARET RICHARDSON
August 2001

Foreword

In his catalogue of sculpture in English country houses, the nineteenth-century scholar Adolph Michaelis expressed a wish that the many collections he had found up and down the land would one day make their way to the metropolis and the British Museum. No doubt, with travels through well-watered meadows and woodlands fresh in mind, he wrote of the 'many brooklets' discharging themselves into 'this mighty stream'. For all their rural charm and his apparent admiration of their creators, Michaelis ultimately disapproved of such private collections. For this pioneer of scientific archaeology, classical antiquity was too serious a matter to be left in the hands of amateurs and their fickle descendants. The fate of the Arundel Marbles was proof of their incompetence: 'The carelessness,' wrote Michaelis, 'with which the venerable relics were allowed to perish was inexcusable, nay absolutely criminal.'

Michaelis' vision of a collection of collections was never to be. Too many of those he saw remained only to be broken up and dispersed in the twentieth-century ruin of the great estates. And yet, others have survived. Spared the political upheavals of the seventeenth century, collections of heavy marbles formed in the eighteenth have often preserved themselves through sheer inertia. Today, knowledge of the collections and the archives that document them has become a specialist field of study. Ruth Guilding, guest curator of this exhibition, is one of its leading scholars. It opens a vista upon some of the most prominent collections, the personalities that formed them, their setting and their *fortuna*. The exhibition is appropriately shown in Sir John Soane's Museum, which under its present and previous dynamic Curators has become a powerful and inspiring force.

DR IAN JENKINS
Keeper, Department of Greek and Roman Antiquities,
The British Museum, London
July 2001

Marble Mania – The Taste for Antique Sculpture

'. . . never forget that the most valuable acquisition a man of refined taste can make is a piece of fine Greek sculpture.'
Gavin Hamilton to Charles Townley, 1771[1]

Marble mania began to infect England in the seventeenth century, reaching its peak at the close of the eighteenth century. During this period, scores of collectors transported antique marbles to England; some were simply following fashionable taste and the market, but a proportion tried to imitate the humanist collectors of the Italian Renaissance or their Roman precursors, with greater or lesser degrees of cognizance.

Nicolo Machiavelli had described the uniquely high value invested in antique sculpture in Italy in *c*.1518, citing in evidence how, 'a bit of old statue has fetched a high price that someone may have it by him to give honour to his house.'[2] In 1634 Henry Peacham adopted the Italian term '*Virtuosi*' to describe the English elite whose collections of classical antiquities, statues, inscriptions curiosities and coins[3] were displayed in cabinets or antiquariums. The term denoted an amateur who delighted in learning or art for its own sake, and continued in use into the late eighteenth century, when the roughly equivalent terms 'dilettante' or 'connoisseur' were substituted.

This pursuit of 'virtu' flourished in the court of James I, and of Charles I, who 'loved sculpture as a connoisseur but exploited it as a king,'[4] becoming a recognised badge of self-distinction. Sculpture formed the currency of diplomatic gifts, furnished royal palaces and great houses, and held first rank in the hierarchy of antiquities. The reputation of Thomas Howard, 14th Earl of Arundel – the first Englishman to form a great collection – as a great statesman and *virtuoso* was founded on his costly purchases of antique sculpture, and his discriminating powers in deploying scholars and friends – Sir Robert Cotton, William Camden, John Evelyn, John Selden and Francis Junius – to publish and interpret them for him. Arundel was himself no scholar, but among rival courtier-collectors such as the 1st Duke of Buckingham and the 4th Earl of Pembroke, he demonstrated a unique ability to exploit and promulgate the claims of his sculpture collection, and its fame, along with that of family seat of Arundel House in the Strand (Figs.1, 2) spread throughout Europe.[5]

Arundel and his wife the Countess Aletheia had spent a year in Italy in 1613–14 travelling with his 'good friend,' the architect Inigo Jones, and returned determined to become a cultural patron in the Italian mould. Thereafter antique culture provided the matrix for the roles which Arundel pursued in public and private. The works of learning produced by Arundel's 'Academie' provided him both with the moral justification for his collecting, and a philosophy of the relevance of the governance and culture of Greece and Rome to the needs of Jacobean England. Selden transcribed Arundel's antique inscriptions to produce the *Marmora Arundeliana* (1628) (Cat.10) and his knowledge of ancient constitutional law thereby derived served as a yardstick for the new legislation enacted by parliament. Above the entrance to the Sculpture Gallery at Arundel House, the antiquary William Camden devised a Latin inscription which proclaimed that Arundel was building upon precedents established by his ancestors, by transporting antiquities from the ruins of Rome to the palaces of the Arundel Howards.[6]

The business of collecting antique sculpture was, from the first, one of 'dead costliness.'[7] As contemporary commentators frequently pointed out, collectors laboured under an onus to demonstrate taste, utility and universal benefits, rather than simply practising conspicuous consumption. In his will drafted in 1617, Arundel had self-consciously imitated the practices which he had observed at the *Marciana Statuario Pubblico* in Venice, the public sculpture gallery formed out of the Grimani family's collection and donated to the city-state, in making the provision that 'all gentlemen of Vertue or Artistes wch are honest men may allways be used with curtesy and humanity when they shall come to see the collections at Arundel House'.[8] His friend John Evelyn sought to perpetuate this practice in establishing a public garden-museum of Arundel's inscriptions in the City of Oxford after his death (Cats.16–18).

The earl died abroad in exile in 1646, and the house of learning which he had constructed was arbitrarily dismantled and plundered during and after the Commonwealth, with his sculptures variously divided up and sold, donated, lost or buried (Cats.1, 3, 4, 11–29). The generation of collectors who came after him, and particularly the 8th Earl of Pembroke, purchaser of about half of the Arundel Marbles, was taxed by the perennial concern of the 'discourse' of civic humanism[9] (promulgated by Lord Shaftesbury, Jonathan Richardson and others): the proper application of taste in the liberal arts, and its potential to teach public virtue, for the greater benefit of Society. Great private palaces and their contents were transmogrified into 'Academies' founded for the public good, the foremost of these being Lord Pembroke's seat of Wilton House. Between c.1700–1750 a stream of written and printed descriptions poured forth from guests, antiquarians and quondam employees about the house (George Vertue, William Stukeley (Cats.22, 23) and Daniel Defoe; Sir Andrew Fountaine and Richard Cowdray (Cat.34)) lauding the 8th Earl's vast acquisitions, and representing the house as a repository that 'does honour to the nation,' countering Alexander Pope's slanders of 'Vanity' and 'Expense'[10] published in his 'Epistle to Lord Burlington.'

Early in the eighteenth century the Grand Tour had become fundamentally important in transporting Italian cultural taste to a broader social base in England, from aristocrats to students of architecture. Young travellers saw the Renaissance collections of Roman sculptures which had been assembled by Italian princes and noblemen in their houses (notably those of the Palazzo Mattei, the Villa Medici (Cat.7) and the Villa Borghese, the gardens of Cardinal Cesi (Fig.3) and of the Cortile Belvedere, housing the papal collections), creating a historicist link with the values of ancient Rome, and sought the satisfaction of furnishing their own houses in the same way. The values invested in antique sculpture could be overlapping and diverse: as grand furniture, history pieces, putative ancestors, exemplars for art and artists and literally 'pieces of vertue.' Transferred to the context of the English country house, these emblems of an élite classical culture

FIGS. 1 & 2 Portraits of the 14th Earl of Arundel and his wife, Countess Aletheia, by George Vertue, after Daniel Mytens. 1745/6. Watercolours, both 305 × 240 (Arundel Castle). The earl is posed in front of his Gallery of antique sculpture, the countess sits in the Picture Gallery with a vignette of the gardens of Arundel House beyond. (By kind permission of the Duke of Norfolk)

could also be a useful tool in the hands of ancestor worshippers, parvenus and the newly ennobled.

Classical sculpture was collected to be seen, and the way in which it was displayed was of consummate importance. Cognoscenti such as Lord Burlington and Thomas Coke plundered Vitruvius and Palladio for architectural precedents, arriving at the repetitive and tightly controlled neo-Roman symmetry of the new Palladianism, with niches, arches and façades which demanded busts and full-length classical statues or casts, rather than the varieties of sculpture featured in earlier collections. From the 1750s limited sets of casts of some of the most famous statues in the antique canon were supplied by Matthew Brettingham the Younger and Joseph Wilton to meet this growing demand.[11] By comparison with antiquities, casts were considerably cheaper and lent themselves to the tidy symmetrical arrangements of Palladian interiors, but although they were sometimes used alongside antiquities (c.f. Holkham Hall, Wentworth Woodhouse, Syon House) their cachet was never so high and they were frequently

relegated to the less significant spaces of the house. These formats were pressed into service by the political supporters of the Augustan Whig faction: at Holkham Hall (Fig.4), Houghton Hall (Fig.5), Wentworth Woodhouse, Farnborough Hall (Fig.6), and Petworth House (Fig.7) antique sculptures or casts were ostentatiously sited on parapets, in galleries and above all, in entrance halls, in a bold assertion of political and cultural affiliation.

With the exception of the short-lived Academy founded by the Duke of Richmond there was no collection of casts or statues available for public consumption to compare with the rich collections enshrined in private houses. Although these could be visited, an inevitable bias operated in favour of persons of the first rank, notable connoisseurs and artists: Lord Leicester's widow opened Holkham Hall on every day except Sunday to 'noblemen and foreignors' and on Tuesdays only to 'other people.'[12] The Society of Dilettanti, whose combined membership owned almost all of the antiquities which were imported throughout the century, briefly proposed founding a

FIG. 3 *View of Cardinal Cesi's Antique Sculpture Garden*, by Hendrick van Cleef III. Signed and dated 1584. Panel, 615 × 1070 (National Gallery of Prague) These gardens, which ranked second only to the papal Sculpture Garden in the Vatican Belvedere, contained a huge collection of antique sculpture amassed during the 1520s by Cardinal Paolo Emilio Cesi, and restored and reorganised by his brother, Cardinal Federico Cesi in the 1540s.

FIG. 4 The Sculpture Gallery, Holkham Hall (Holkham Hall)

FIG. 6 The Entrance Hall, Farnborough Hall (National Trust Photographic Library/Angelo Hornak)

FIG. 7 The North Gallery, Petworth House (National Trust Photographic Library/Andreas von Einsiedel)

FIG. 5 The Stone Hall, Houghton Hall (A. F. Kersting)

FIG. 8 The Marble Hall, Kedleston Hall, built to designs by Robert Adam in the 1760s and completed in *c.*1777 (National Trust Photographic Library/Nadia MacKenzie)

FIG. 9 *Frammenti delle Camere sepolcrali de' Liberti, e Servi ec. Della Famiglia di Augusto* from *Le Antichità Romane* by G. B. Piranesi, Vol.III (1756) Plate XXIX

FIG. 10 A guide showing a tourist the inside of a sepulchral vault, in an engraving by Carlo Labruzzi taken from *Via Appia illustrata ab urbe Roma ad Capuam*, (Rome 1794) Plate 8

cast collection 'in order to produce something from this society that may be beneficiall to the publick,'[13] but neither this nor the museum of members' sculpture proposed in *c*.1784 was carried out.

Robert Adam's designs for ostentatious interiors at Kedleston Hall (Fig.8) and Syon House deployed the same architectural vocabulary used at Holkham Hall, and marked a departure only in the richness and variety of antique architectural ornament used, and in the partial superimposition of antique plan-forms on existing structures. One functioned as a country house and the other as a suburban villa, but both depended on copies of antique sculpture for lavish ornament, plaster casts being almost exclusively used at Kedleston (Cat.47), and more expensive marble and bronze copies (supported by further antiques and plaster casts) at Syon (Cat.43).

By the 1760s, collecting antique sculpture had become a branch of archaeology, systematised by the publication of Johann Winckelmann's new methodological art history[14] and fuelled by the picturesque aesthetic of Giovanni Battista Piranesi's images (Fig.9). Frequent communications and transactions took place among a small well-informed coterie in Rome, Naples and England, notably the dealers Gavin Hamilton and Thomas Jenkins, the sculptor-restorers G. B. Piranesi, Bartolomeo Cavaceppi and Joseph Nollekens, the scholars J. J. Winckelmann and the 'Baron' d'Hancarville and the collectors Sir William Hamilton, Cardinal Albani, Charles Townley and Lyde Browne. The archaeological circumstances in which antiquities were discovered (Fig.10) were communicated to the fellows of the Society of Antiquaries in London in letters sent from Jenkins or Winckelmann in Rome, or reported verbally by the collector–speculator Lyde Browne.[15] British collectors were also highly susceptible to the taste manifested by successive popes, who now began to exercise their right to first choice of the marbles reaching the market from private collections and new excavations: Clement XIV established a new museum of classical antiquities in the Vatican in *c.*1771, completed by his successor Pius VI, where antique fragments and sepulchral monuments served as pedestals, (Fig.11) a return to Renaissance practice which was swiftly adopted in England.

The architect Robert Adam's response to the new antiquarianism was to design a columbarium-museum of antiquities for the Long Gallery at Syon *c.*1764 (Cat.50), and a 'Rock Room,' proposed for one of the pavilions at Kedleston (Cat.60). Neither was fully carried out, but both were prescient in catering for the renaissance of a taste for more diverse pieces – sarcophagi, urns, ash-chests, candelabra and 'Etruscan' painted vases – at a time when the price of marble antiquities was soaring and Roman dealers complained of the scarcity of good full-length figure sculpture. Here Piranesi's role as catalyst in this

FIG. 11 Antique Candelabra, including one of the Barberini Candelabra (left), seen in Vincenzo Feoli's *Veduta prospettica del la Galleria de Vasi e Candelabri,* (1795) in the Museo Pio-Clementino founded by Clement XIV in 1771 (Archivi Alinari – Firenze)

shift of taste, through the sale of his publications and of his fabricated marble antiquities (Cat.65) was seminal in creating a new market for such pieces. Both the collection acquired *en bloc* in 1765 by the parvenu landowner William Weddell from the dealer Thomas Jenkins in Rome, and that bought more thoughtfully from Gavin Hamilton one year earlier by the 2nd Viscount Palmerston contained Piranesi's cannibalised fabrications, as well as antique sarcophagi panels, cineraria and altars.

The paradox of connoisseurship in the late eighteenth century 'was that while it professed a mission to educate a greater public, it defined itself by its exclusivity,'[16] evidenced by the nonpareil, scholarly collectors who brought a degree of fanaticism to the role. The Enlightenment figures Charles Townley (Fig.12) and Sir William Hamilton made their reputations from their collections, now classified and presented on a more systematic basis in publications written or 'ghosted' by scholars such as d'Hancarville. Townley's famous marble collection at his Park Street house-museum in Westminster (Cats.71, 72) inspired a host of imitators including Sir Richard Worsley, William Petty, 1st Marquess of Lansdowne, John Campbell, 1st Baron Cawdor and Henry Blundell, whose collections were displayed in 'museum rooms' rather than galleries; and personal museums were also amassed by a class of semi-professional collectors such as G. B. Piranesi, Robert Adam (Cat.59) ,Thomas Jenkins, C. H. Tatham and Antonio Canova (Cats.88–95).

Robert Adam's Sculpture Gallery for Weddell at Newby Hall of *c.*1767 (Fig.13) was one of the last to be established before the advent of the taste-maker, Charles Townley. When Townley came to design the interiors of his house-museum he rejected the 'pseudo-archaeology' of the Newby gallery in favour of more associative and flexible interiors where methodology could govern display, featuring top-lighting and plain walls against which the sculpture was shown to best advantage.[17] When the British Museum's new galleries for sculpture were designed in *c.*1805 Townley's principles were adopted wholesale (Cats.81, 97, 98).

Townley had aped the practices of the great collector Cardinal Albani, in attempting to garner a 'complete' collection of ancient marbles, from every phase of historical development as it was then understood, which could provide an illustration of 'the History of the Art.'

FIG. 12 Charles Townley's Library at 7, Park Street Westminster, by Johan Zoffany, 1781–3. Oil on canvas, 1270 × 990. (Towneley Hall Art Gallery, Burnley)

For this reason he employed the Baron d'Hancarville, both in the causes of research and scholarship, but also to perform the service which Winckelmann had provided for the papal collections, to apotheosise Townley's marbles and with them his memory, for posterity.[18] Townley's decision to bestow his precious collection on the British Museum was a further step towards this goal, only to be withdrawn when he believed that its future might instead be secured at Towneley Hall (Fig.14) (Cat.73).

His other endowment to scholarship, d'Hancarville's *Recherches sur l'Origine, l'Esprit et les Progrès des Arts de la Grèce* (1785–6) (Cat.82) which he partially financed, was more influential for a later generation of collectors. The overt symbolism adopted by Thomas Hope for the decoration of his house at Duchess Street demonstrated a close knowledge of the theories rehearsed in the *Recherches*,[19] and of the decorative schemes devised for Park Street. Sir John Soane also painstakingly studied his copy of the work, which convinced him of the symbolical significance

FIG. 13 View looking down the Sculpture Gallery at Newby Hall, designed by Robert Adam *c*. 1767 (Newby Hall)

FIG. 14 The Sculpture Rotunda designed for Towneley Hall by Joseph Bonomi, *c*.1783 (Cat.73) (Private Collection)

of ornament in ancient civilisations,[20] a fundamental principle for his architectural practice, and for the interiors which he created in his house at Lincoln's Inn Fields. Soane shared Townley and d'Hancarville's obsession with a return to origins, manifested in the various sepulchral ensembles which he created (Cat.61). By the end of his life the first place in his collections, his museum of sculpture in the 'Plaister Room' or Dome (as it was later called), had evolved into a sculptural 'Pantheon' to include the finest figurative works in his collection presided over by statuettes of Raphael and Michelangelo by Flaxman and Chantrey's bust of Soane himself, the latter standing upon a lion monopodium – d'Hancarville's 'lion symbol of the *soleil diurne* who spreads light . . .'[21]

Amongst the high aristocracy, where the desire to lead taste and promote British artists was prevalent, the latest sculpture galleries were presented as repositories for antiquities juxtaposed with modern neo-classical works (Fig.15), standing as exemplars and manifestos for the national school. From the 1820s the 3rd Earl of Egremont (Fig.16) used his father's antique sculpture at Petworth as the motif on which his patronage of modern British sculptors was founded (Cats.104, 108, 109); at Chatsworth the 6th Duke of Devonshire formed a neo-classical sculpture gallery in homage to Canova from 1823–33 (Fig.17) (Cats.102, 103, 111); and at Woburn, the presentation of the antique marbles and contemporary works which the 5th Duke of Bedford had collected between about 1800–1830 was gradually formalised to create a series of complex political and symbolical narratives (Cats.99, 100, 101).

At the close of the eighteenth century, the political

FIG. 15 The Painted Hall at Chatsworth House, by William Hunt, 1827, with Gibson's group of Mars and Cupid and antique busts, some formerly at Chiswick House. Watercolour, 530 × 430 (Devonshire Collection, Chatsworth)

FIG. 16 The 3rd Earl of Egremont in the North Gallery at Petworth House with neoclassical sculptures by Carew and Flaxman behind him, a posthumous portrait by Thomas Phillips, after 1837. Oil on canvas, 1.86 × 1.55 m (National Trust Photographic Library/John Hammond)

FIG. 17 The 6th Duke's Sculpture Gallery at Chatsworth House photographed in 1876, Canova's Endymion in the foreground (Devonshire Collection, Chatsworth)

resonances associated with classical sculpture had begun to be eroded and replaced by more romantic or idiosyncratic personal constructs. Prince Albert, the Prince Consort, adopted the Italianate neo-Renaissance style, filtered through the Teutonic scholasticism of his native country, to create the Sculpture Corridor in his seaside palace at Osborne (Fig.18) (Cats.105, 107), where Raphaelesque polychrome and antique sculpture dignified and endorsed the contemporary 'romantic' pieces which the royal couple liked to exchange as birthday presents, and portrait sculptures of themselves. Gothic architecture provided a frame for classical sculpture at Arbury Hall (Cat.114) where the house's historical character took precedence over Roman architectural taste, at Mamhead, peopled with historical statues of the fictional date of

the house (Cat.115), and at Wilton House, where the imagined *genius loci*, Scheemaker's statue of Shakespeare, was given a Tudorbethan setting in the early 1800s (Fig.19) (Cat.113), at the same time as the classical marbles were demoted to Wyatt's Gothic Cloister

Thus the sculpted deity of antiquity resigned his place to the English poet as hero, and the Augustan Age to the Chivalric Revival. A few of the collections of antique sculpture formed with so determined an intellectual or political agenda in the seventeenth, eighteenth and early nineteenth centuries waited in their dusty country house galleries. The majority, sold up, dispersed, and subject to the museum culture of a later age, were eventually neutralised and aetheticised, on becoming cultural properties which were no longer in privileged private ownership.

FIG. 18 The Marble Corridor, Osborne House, designed and furnished by the Prince Consort and Ludwig Gruner c.1845–1856 (© Crown copyright.NMR)

FIG. 19 Design for a Shakespeare Niche at Wilton House, attributed to Sir Richard Westmacott, c.1812–1826 (Cat.113) (The Collection of the Earl of Pembroke)

Notes

1 British Museum, Central Archive, Townley Papers, TY7/638.

2 N. Machievelli, *The Discourses*, Book 1, (c.1518).

3 H. Peacham, *The Compleat Gentlemen*, (1634), (G. S. Gordon ed.) (1905) pp.104–5.

4 D. Howarth, 'Charles I, Sculpture and Sculptors,' in A. Macgregor (ed.) *The late King's Goods*, (Oxford 1989) p.78.

5 A. Michaelis, *Ancient Marbles in Great Britain*, (Cambridge 1882) p.25, fn.45.

6 British Library, Add MS. 36,294, f.65b.

7 Peacham, (1906) pp.104–5.

8 J. Fletcher, 'The Arundels in the Veneto,' *Apollo* 144 (August 1996) p.81.

9 J. Barrell, *The Political Theory of Painting from Reynolds to Hazlitt*, (New Haven and London 1986) pp.3–23.

10 Epistle IV, to Richard Boyle, Earl of Burlington, in: *Pope, Poetical Works*, H. Davis, (ed.) (Oxford 1966) pp.314–321.

11 J. Kenworthy Browne, 'Matthew Brettingham's Rome Account Book,' *Walpole Society XLIX* (1983) pp.42–44.

12 *The Norwich Tour or Travellers Pocket Companion . . . in the County of Norfolk*, (Norwich 1786, 1795, 1808).

13 L. Cust, *History of the Society of Dilettanti*, (London 1898), p.59.

14 J. J. Winckelmann, *Geschicte der Kunst des Alterthums*, 2 vols, (Dresden 1764); *Monumenti antichi inediti*, 2 vols, (Rome 1767).

15 Library of the Society of Antiquaries, Minute Book ,VIII, pp.343–9; S.R.Pierce, 'Thomas Jenkins in Rome,' *Journal of the Society of Antiquaries*, 45, (1965) pp.200–229.

16 I. Jenkins, 'Seeking the Bubble Reputation,' *Journal of the History of Collections* 9,2, (1997) p.201.

17 I. Jenkins in A. Wilton and I. Bignamini (eds.) *Grand Tour, The Lure of Italy in the Eighteenth Century* (Tate Gallery 1997) pp.258–260.

18 British Museum, Central Archives, Townley Papers, TY1/17/1, d'Hancarville to Townley, n.d.

19 D. Watkin, 'Thomas Hope, John Soane and Sculpture,' unpublished lecture given at the Mellon Centre, 1997.

20 D. Watkin, 'The Symbolical Language of Antiquity,' in *Sir John Soane, Enlightenment Thought and the Royal Academy Lectures*, (Cambridge 1996) pp.262–4.

21 Watkin (1996) pp.265, fn.41.

Lenders to the Exhibition

The Duke of Norfolk; The British Museum; The visitors of the Ashmolean Museum; The National Portrait Gallery; Mr David Sturdy; The Governing Body of Christ Church Oxford; The Duke and Duchess of Devonshire; The Bodleian Library; The Earl of Pembroke; The British Library; The Earl of Leicester; London Borough of Lambeth Archives Department, Minet Library; The Society of Antiquaries of London; The National Trust; Mr Ian Scott; Lord Romsey; Lord Egremont; The Lewis Walpole Library, Yale University; The Duke of Northumberland; Sheffield City Archives; Mr Glynn Boyd Harte; The Hon. Simon Howard; Dr John Martin Robinson; West Yorkshire Archives, Leeds; Towneley Hall Art Gallery, Burnley; The Dowager Duchess of Cawdor; Dr Ruth Guilding; The London Library; The Royal Academy of Arts; The Henry Moore Institute, Leeds; Her Majesty the Queen; Tate Britain; Mr Charles Hind; Royal Institute of British Architects Drawings Collection

Cataloguing Note

All measurements are given as
height × width × depth, in millimetres.

Abbreviated References

R. Chandler, *Marmora Oxoniensa*, Oxford 1763 cited as Chandler

A. Michaelis, *Ancient Marbles in Great Britain* (Cambridge, 1882) cited as Michaelis

The Catalogue

FIG. 20. *The Connoisseur*, James Stephanoff, 1817 (Cat.119)

1 Colossal right foot in a sandal

Broken at the ankle, the ends of the first two toes missing
Marble, 230 × 565 × 255
Hellenistic / Roman period
Arundel Castle
By kind permission of the Duke of Norfolk
Lit. M. J. Hammerson and B. F. Cook in *Transactions of the London and Middlesex Archaeological Society*, v.26, 1975, pp.209–248

This was one of seven classical marbles which were excavated in 1972 from the former site of Arundel House in the Strand in London. It can be presumed to have belonged to Thomas Howard (1585–1646), Earl of Arundel and Surrey, who assembled the first substantial collection of classical sculpture and inscriptions in England, the so-called Arundel Marbles (Cats.3, 4, 11–12, 13–15, 27–29), housed in a gallery within the house and in gardens sloping down to the river. After his death the collection was neglected and then dispersed among several new owners; a residue of unwanted pieces remained and were buried beneath the house when it was demolished in 1680–2.

There is no trace of a plinth under the foot, which is therefore unlikely to have been broken from a statue, and may have been made as a votive piece.

2 Colossal right foot in a sandal

Broken at the ankle
Marble, 520 × 870 × 350
Rome, first to second century AD
British Museum, GR 1784. 1-31.5 (BM Sculpture 2109)
The British Museum, London
Lit. I. Jenkins and K. Sloan, *Vases and Volcanoes, Sir William Hamilton and his Collection*, (British Museum 1996) cat.133 / pp.59–60, 229

Given to the British Museum by Sir William Hamilton in 1784, this was among a group of valuable pieces of sculpture gathered in Italy while he was serving as the British Envoy at the court of Naples, with the specific intention of presenting them to the British Museum, to be displayed alongside the his first collection of antiquities, bought by the Museum in 1772. Sir William served as a Trustee of the Museum (previously a repository for books and natural history specimens) from 1783–1803, and his collections and benefactions greatly influenced its developing collecting policy towards further acquisitions of this type.

CAT. 1 *Colossal right foot in a sandal*

CAT. 2 *Colossal right foot in a sandal* (The British Museum, London)

3 Fragment of a colossal foot

Marble, 176 × 195 × 325
Roman Imperial period
Ashmolean Museum, G1202
Visitors of the Ashmolean Museum

Presumed to have been among the collection of marbles made by Thomas Howard (1585–1646), Earl of Arundel and Surrey, a large number of which were subsequently purchased in 1691 for £300 by Sir William Fermor, for display at his country house, Easton Neston in Northamptonshire (see Cats.25, 26). When Fermor's grandson George, 2nd Earl of Pomfret was about to sell them to cover debts, the marbles were purchased and preserved by his mother Henrietta, the Dowager Countess of Pomfret, and in 1755 she presented them to the University of Oxford. There they were united with the inscriptions and incised stones from the gardens of Arundel House rescued by John Evelyn, which had come to the University in 1667 (Cats.13–15, 28, 29).

4 Sleeping Eros upon a Lion Skin

Lacking right hand, a piece of the left arm and the left foot
Marble, 250 × 695 × 365
Roman 1st–3rd century AD
Ashmolean Museum, Michaelis 37
Visitors of the Ashmolean Museum
Lit. Michaelis 37; Chandler 49; B. A. Baily, (ed). 'Northamptonshire in the early Eighteenth Century,' *Northamptonshire Records Society*, vol.39, 1996, p.67

This is another of the marbles formerly in the Arundel collection, removed to Easton Neston in 1692 and subsequently presented to the University of Oxford by the Dowager Countess of Pomfret in 1755. The sculpture was one of many displayed in the gardens at Easton Neston, where it was sketched by the artist Peter Tillemans in c.1719 (BL Add Mss. 32457, B L 57); it was also the subject of a learned essay (*An Essay on a Sleeping Cupid, Being One of the Arundelian Marbles . . .*) published in 1755 by the antiquarian John Nixon, Rector of Cold Higham in Northamptonshire.

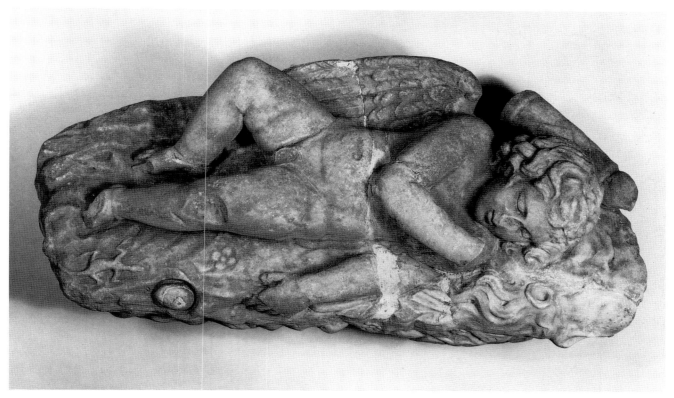

CAT. 4 *Sleeping Eros upon a Lion Skin* (Visitors of the Ashmolean Museum)

Arundel and Italy

5–6 W. H. Worthington, after Daniel Mytens
Thomas Howard, 2nd Earl of Arundel and Surrey
Aletheia, Countess of Arundel and Surrey

Inscribed *Copied by R. J. Bone and Engraved by
W. H. Worthington*
Engravings, both 107 × 100
By courtesy of the National Portrait Gallery, London

Antique culture provided a matrix for Arundel's role in
private and public life. Within the earl's intellectual circle,
his pictures and sculptures were represented as having
been assembled for the greater national good, and his
sculpture gallery seems to have served as a site where
political associates such as Thomas Wentworth, 1st Earl
of Strafford, habitually came to discuss policy and polity
beneath the gaze of ancient worthies, rulers and deities
(D. Howarth, *Lord Arundel and his Circle*, (New Haven &
London, 1985) p.80), as well as offering a unique resource
for 'gentlemen of vertue and Artistes wch are honest'.
Daniel Mytens's portraits of the earl and countess painted
around 1618 portray the pair amongst emblems of humanist
culture, the earl gravely pointing to the 'pieces of vertue'
which were credited with the power to inspire 'virtuous'
actions (Figs 1, 2). More sculpture was placed in the garden
beyond the picture gallery, perhaps in the topiary niches
which close the vista in Mytens's portrait of the Countess
Aletheia, devices which Arundel may also have seen and
copied from Italian gardens such as those of the Villa
Medici.

7 *The Villa Medici, c.1920*

Photographic print
Archivi Alinari – Firenze

For those who had travelled to Italy in the seventeenth
century, the displays of classical inscriptions set into the
walls of the gardens at Arundel House must have recalled
Italian Renaissance precedents. John Evelyn, a founder
member of the Royal Society, which met at Arundel House,
had noted similar arrangements at the Villa Borghese in
1644, and at the Villa Medici, where: 'the whole outside
of this facciata is [encrusted] with antique and rare
Basse-relievis and statues' (Evelyn, *Diary* 1644, Nov. 8).

8 Hieronymus Cock (1510–70), after Marten van Heemskerck
The Statue Court of the Palazzo Valle in Rome, 1553

Engraving, 287 × 416
Signed and dated lower right
British Museum, Department of Prints and Drawings
1871-12-9-4637
The British Museum, London
Lit. P. P. Bober and R. Rubenstein, *Renaissance Artists and
Antique Sculpture*, (Oxford, 1987) pp.479–80

The bulk of this large collection was amassed by Cardinal
Andrea della Valle (1463–1534) building on an existing
family collection, and the courtyard in his new palace on
the Via Papale (now the Corso Vittorio Emmanuele) was
laid out as a showplace for ancient statuary. In 1584 most
of the collection was purchased by Ferdinando de Medici,
to be used in the embellishment of the Villa Medici in the
Pincio in Rome, and some of the Valle bas-reliefs were
embedded in the façade walls of the Villa, where a
proportion of them remain to this day (see Cat.7).

CAT. 7 *Villa Medici*, c.1920. Much of the sculpture adorning the garden
front was taken down in the 1780s. (Archivi Alinari – Firenze)

HÆC VISVNTVR ROMÆ, IN HORTO CARD· A VALLE, EIVS BENEFICIO, EX ANTIQVITATIS· RELIQVIIS IBIDEM CONSERVATA·

CAT. 8 *The Statue Court of the Palazzo Valle in Rome*, 1553 (The British Museum, London)

9 Dirck Volkertsz Coornhert (*c.*1519–90)
The Statue Court of the Casa Sassi, Rome, 1553

Engraving, 378 × 300
Signed and dated 'DVC 53' in medallion, upper left
British Museum, Department of Prints and Drawings,
1928-3-13-176
The British Museum, London
Lit. P. P. Bober and R. Rubenstein, *Renaissance Artists and
Antique Sculpture*, (Oxford, 1987) p.479; R. Rubenstein in
Festschrift fur Matthias Winner, eds. V. V. Fleming and
S. Schutze, (Mainz 1996) pp.230–243

The ancient Roman family of Sassi owned a significant
antique sculpture collection, displayed in the court of their
palace which stood on the present Via del Governo Vecchio
in Parione. In 1546 the collection was sold to the Farnese,
and in the late eighteenth century the finest pieces were
transported to Naples, where they eventually joined the
antiquities furnishing the new royal museum there (now
the National Archaeological Museum), founded by
Ferdinand IV.

10 John Selden (1584–1654)
Marmora Arundeliana, 1628

Printed book, rebound nineteenth century in half calf
bindings and marbled paper, 220 × 167
Arundel Castle Library
By kind permission of the Duke of Norfolk

Selden's publication celebrated the arrival at Arundel House
of a consignment of about two hundred antique marbles,
many of them ancient Greek inscriptions collected for
Arundel in Asia Minor and Greece by his chaplain, the classical scholar William Petty. In the foreword to this work,
Selden described how Sir Robert Cotton had arrived at his
house late one night, and insisted on immediately returning
to Arundel House to show him these 'treasures.' At dawn
the following morning, Selden, helped by Richard James,
and the Royal Librarian Francis Junius, had at once begun
the work of washing and deciphering the inscriptions.
Among these was the Parian Chronicle, 264–3 BC (now in
the Ashmolean Museum), a stone fragment with archaic
script, translated by Selden, which described the workings
of the Greek city states. This publication spread the fame
of Arundel's collection throughout learned Europe.

Lord Arundel's Marbles Dispersed

11 *Bearded Head*

Late Hellenistic or Roman
Marble, 440 × 350 × 200
Ashmolean Museum, 1994.45
Visitors of the Ashmolean Museum
Lit. John Aubrey, *The Natural History and Antiquities of Surrey*, (1719) pp.282–4

This fragment was among twenty-seven pieces formerly at Arundel House, which had been transferred to a pleasure-garden, Cuper or Cupid's Gardens on Lambeth embankment, by the early eighteenth century. John Aubrey included illustrations of them in his *Natural History and Antiquities of Surrey*, (1719), and noted that 'being imperfect, and very much injured by time, they were not thought valuable enough for a Present to the University of Oxford . . . they were therefore, when Arundell House was turned into a Street, removed hither, where they received very ill Usage from the Ignorance and Stupidity of those who knew not their Value, and are still exposed to the open Air, and Folly of Passers by.' The head was acquired by the Ashmolean Museum in 1994.

12 *Head of Meleager*

Marble, 420 × 220 × 270 (inc. pedestal)
Roman copy of a Greek original
Ashmolean Museum, Michaelis 71
Visitors of the Ashmolean Museum
Lit. Michaelis 71

This head, formerly in the Arundel Collection, was also among the Countess of Pomfret's donation of marbles to the University of Oxford, made in 1755 (Cats.3, 4, 27). These pieces had previously been restored for display at Easton Neston House by the Italian sculptor Giovanni Baptista Guelfi, the heads typically being set on new marble busts with a socle base, but in the nineteenth century these restorations were removed.

13–15 *Three Inscribed stones*

Marble, 210 × 250 × 120; 415 × 240 × 110; 212 × 350 × 70
Roman Imperial period
Ashmolean Museum, AN C. 3.13; AN C. 3.104; AN C.3.111
Visitors of the Ashmolean Museum
Lit. Chandler. 3. 13, 3. 111, 3. 104

In 1634 Henry Peacham had written :

> Arundel-House is the chief English scene of ancient inscription . . . You shall find all the walles of the house inlayde with them and speaking Greeke and Latine to you. The garden especially will afford you the pleasure of a world of Learned Lectures in this kind. The use of these memorials tends to the illustration of Historye, and of antiquitie of divers matters, places and Cities . . . (Peacham, (1906) p. 112)

By 1667 John Evelyn was describing how these inscriptions were 'miserably neglected and scattered up and down about the garden and other parts of Arundel House . . .' (Evelyn, *Diary* 1678, Aug. 29). These three inscriptions were amongst those which he arranged to be removed to Oxford in 1668 (Cats.16–17).

16–17 David Loggan (1635–?1700)
The Sheldonian Theatre, Oxford, View from the North
The Sheldonian Theatre, Oxford, View from the South

from *Oxonia Illustrata* (1675)
Engravings, both 520 × 600
By kind permission of Mr David Sturdy
Lit. D. Sturdy and N. Moorcraft, 'Christopher Wren and Oxford's Garden of Antiquities,' *Minerva* vol. 10 no. 1 (Jan/Feb 1999) pp.25–28

John Evelyn was anxious to commemorate the man whom he referred to as 'the magnificent Earle of Arundel, Thomas Earl Marshall of England, my noble friend whilst he lived.' He perhaps regarded himself as the earl's successor as arbiter of taste under the restored monarchy of Charles II, for it was at his instigation that the Arundel inscriptions became more genuinely publicly available, when they were placed in a 'museum' setting in 1668, arranged by Christopher Wren in niches in the precinct wall around his new Sheldonian Theatre. Here they joined a small collection of inscriptions donated to the university by Arundel's friend the scholar John Selden, the author of

CAT. 16   *The Sheldonian Theatre, Oxford, View from the North*

Marmora Arundeliana, (1628) (Cat.10) Loggan's two views of the 'Theatre Yard' occur in a series of forty plates celebrating the University made for subscribers, or for presentation to important visitors.

18   Humphrey Prideaux (1648–1724)
Marmora Oxoniensia, 1676

Proof plate, 346 × 317
Christ Church Oxford, Aldrich Prints x.3.73
Lit. D.Sturdy and N. Moorcraft, 'Christopher Wren and Oxford's Garden of Antiquities,' *Minerva* vol. 10 no. 1 (Jan/Feb 1999) pp.25–28
The Governing Body of Christ Church Oxford

Prideaux's publication of the University of Oxford's classical inscriptions, the *Marmora Oxoniensia*, included those taken from the gardens of Arundel House after John Evelyn had intervened to save them from destruction:

> 'and whatever I found that had inscriptions on them that were not Status . . . getting them removed and piled together, with those which were incrusted in the Garden walles, I sent immediately letters to the Vice-Chancellor what I had procured, and that if they esteemed it a service to the University (of which I had been a member) they should take orders for their transportation' (Evelyn, *Diary* 1667, Sept. 19).

This proof plate, intended for the publication, but not used, shows some of the inscriptions as they were arranged in one bay of the (now demolished) east wall around the Sheldonian Theatre (Cats.16–17).

19   James Green
after Samuel Wale (d.1786)
Allegorical View of the Arundel Statues

from *The Oxford Almanack*, 1757
Engraving, 560 × 490
By kind permission of Mr David Sturdy

This view depicts some of the finest of the Arundel marbles brought to Oxford through the Pomfret bequest, standing in an imaginary landscape, amongst ancient temples and ruins and a large building of the Pantheon type. Minerva is shown leading the personification of the University and her three Faculties out of their 'Gothic Retirement,' to be introduced to figures representing Antiquity, Sculpture and Architecture. On the left 'Time' is prevented from destroying an ancient Arundelian inscription by the 'Genius of Antique Learning,' who leads up 'History' to consult the inscription. The sculptural group of Hercules and a Lion, formerly in the Pomfret Collection at Eastern Neston, (Cat.27) can be seen balanced on the cornice of a ruined amphitheatre.

CAT. 19   *Allegorical View of the Arundel Statues*

20 Jacques Rigaud (c.1681–1754)
Chiswick, View from in front of the Burlington Lane at the rond-point with obelisk, looking along three alleys

Watercolour, 279 × 508
Chatsworth House, Inventory no. W. C. 154
Devonshire Collection, Chatsworth. Lent by the Duke
of Devonshire and the Chatsworth Settlement
Lit. *Archaeology*, XXI, 1968, p.210; R. Hewlings, *Chiswick House
and Gardens* (English Heritage 1989) p.31; John Harris,
*The Palladian Revival, Lord Burlington, His Villa and Garden
at Chiswick*, (New Haven and London 1994) p.223

Rigaud's view shows the obelisk which had been erected
in the gardens of Chiswick House by 1733, with an antique
bas-relief of a Roman wedding from the Arundel collection,
set into the pedestal. The *Gentleman's Magazine* of July 1769
stated that the relief was given to the 3rd Earl of Burlington
in 1712 with other fragments of the Arundel marbles by a
Mr Theobald, who had dug them up near the site of the
now demolished Arundel House off the Strand.

21 Allan Ramsay (1713–1784)
Dr Richard Mead, 1740

Oil on canvas 1264 × 1001
By courtesy of the National Portrait Gallery, London
Lit. M. Webster, 'Taste of an Augustan Collector,' in *Country
Life* CXLVII (29 January 1970) pp.249–50; A. Smart, *Allan
Ramsay: A Complete Catalogue of his Paintings* (J. Ingamells,
ed.) (New Haven and London 1999) p.157, fig.47

CAT. 21 *Dr Richard Mead*, 1740 (National Portrait Gallery, London)

CAT. 20 *Chiswick, View from in front of the Burlington Lane at the
rond-point with obelisk, looking along three alleys* (Devonshire Collection,
Chatsworth)

Mead (1673–1754) who became physician in ordinary
to George II in 1727, was also a celebrated collector of art
antiquities and natural history specimens. From 1720 he
lived in Great Ormond Street, where part of his collection
was displayed in a garden gallery to which visitors were
admitted. Ramsay painted Mead posed in front of a
classical statue of Asclepius, the god of medicine, but also
with his superb bronze bust, the 'Arundel Homer', which
Mead had purchased in 1720 after it had passed by descent
to Arundel's grandson the Earl of Stafford. After Mead's
death in 1754 the bust was acquired by the Earl of Exeter
and then presented to the British Museum, having since
been re-identified as a bust of Sophocles.

22 William Stukeley (1687–1765)
Account of the Statues at Wilton, 1723

Pen and ink, MS. notebook with marbled boards,
205 × 160
The Bodleian Library, University of Oxford, MS. Top. Wilts. e6

The 8th Earl of Pembroke had brought those of Arundel's
antique marbles which had been displayed inside Arundel
House to Wilton House in 1678, and added to these
marbles from the sale of the Giustiniani collection in
Rome, from the Mazarin collection in Paris and from the
Valletta collection in Naples, before his death in 1733. In
1723 the antiquary William Stukeley began writing this
account of the collection for publication, but as he noted
on the inside cover, 'my lord sent for it and transposed the
leaves, put out and in, what he pleased, and so confounded
my scheme that I left it off.' The earl's interpolations and
overwritings in a darker ink occur throughout the text.

23 William Stukeley
Wilton House, Sketch of the Venus Column and the Courtyard, 1724

from '*Drawings of many of Lord Pembrokes antiquitys at Wilton, which I took there in June 1724.*'
Pen, ink and wash, mounted in vellum bound volume, drawing 300 × 195
Inscribed *One of the pillars of the temple of Venus genetrix erected by Julius Caesar, now in the courtyard at Wilton*
The Bodleian Library, University of Oxford, MS. Top. Wilts. C4, f.6
Lit. M. Vickers, 'Two vast and trunkless legs of Stone,' *The Ashmolean* 32 (1997), p.13

This is one of three views in the volume showing the court in front of the eastern, entrance façade of Wilton House in the time of the 8th Earl of Pembroke. Stukeley recorded the settings for statues outside the house, and individual pieces from the vast collection inside, as illustrations for his intended publication of Lord Pembroke's sculpture (Cat.22), begun in the previous year. At the centre of the court before the gateway into the inner quadrangle at Wilton House the earl had set up Arundel's spectacular column of white Egyptian granite, surmounted by a statue of Venus, exactly replicating the way in which it had been displayed in the gardens of Arundel House. John Evelyn had procured this column for Arundel in Rome; transported to Wilton, it acted as an eye-catcher which also sounded a note of Roman triumphalism.

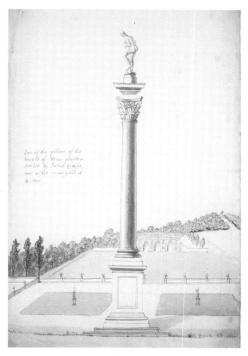

CAT. 23 *Wilton House, Sketch of the Venus Column and the Courtyard*, 1724 (The Bodleian Library, University of Oxford)

24 Unknown hand
A Catalogue of ye Marbles . . . in ye Earl of Pembroke's House at Wilton, eighteenth century

Pen and ink, notebook in marbled paper cover, 210 × 170
Wiltshire Record Office, Wilton House Mss. WHA 2057 H5/10
The Collection of the Earl of Pembroke, Wilton House, Salisbury

This appears to be one of the earliest manuscript guides to the sculpture at Wilton House to be completed (cf. Cat.22), written shortly after the death of the 8th Earl. Its anonymous author was a member of the 8th Earl's intimate circle, which included the Italian antiquary Nicholas Haym, said to have produced such an account based on one written by Earl Thomas himself (G. Richardson, *Aedes Pembrochianae*, Salisbury 1788, Preface), and Sir Andrew Fountaine who contributed to the first published guide (Cat.34). Its author sets out to commemorate and celebrate the earl and the historical imperatives which had guided his taste. The text highlights the educational value and utility of the collection, perhaps in an intended riposte to the poet Alexander Pope's jibes (published in the 'Epistle to Richard Boyle, Earl of Burlington' in 1731) at his 'Vanity of Expense' in amassing 'Statues, dirty gods and Coins.'

25 Peter Tillemans (1684–1734)
Easton Neston, the Arundel Marbles, 'Tomb of Germanicus', July 1719

Pen and wash 315 × 202
British Library Add. Mss. 32467, f. 21
By permission of the British Library
Lit. B. A. Bailey, 'Northamptonshire in the early eighteenth century,' *Northamptonshire Record Society* vol. 39 (1996) p.56; M. Vickers, 'Germanicus' Tomb' in *The Ashmolean* 15 (1988–9), pp.6–8

This assemblage of sculpture which stood at one end of the terrace in the gardens at Easton Neston House in Northamptonshire, took its name from an arrangement in Arundel House which included a sarcophagus supporting a bust supposed to portray the Roman general Germanicus. This composition which resembled the kind of picturesque displays seen by Arundel in the palaces of the Italian nobility, was apparently piously reassembled and embellished when William Fermor, later Lord Lempster, bought the garden statuary from Arundel House for £300 in 1691 and transferred them to his country house of Easton Neston. Here, they were drawn by the artist Peter Tillemans in 1719, and recorded by the antiquary George Vertue in 1734. In c.1988 the sculptural parts of the assemblage were brought together in a partial reconstruction in the Randolph Gallery of the Ashmolean Museum.

CAT. 25 *Easton Neston, the Arundel Marbles, 'Tomb of Germanicus', July 1719 (By permission of the British Library)*

26 Peter Tillemans
Easton Neston, the Arundel Marbles, Fireplace wall of the Entrance Hall, July 1719

Pen and wash 315 × 198
British Library Add. Mss. 32467, f. 51
By permission of the British Library
Lit. B. A. Bailey, 'Northamptonshire in the early eighteenth
century,' *Northamptonshire Record Society* vol. 39 (1996) p.65

The fireplace in the large alcove at the centre of the rear wall of the Hall at Easton Neston supported a statuette of Hercules attacked by a Lion (Cat.27), standing in front of an arrangement of scrolls and a back panel variously attributed to the restorer Giovanni Guelfi or to William Kent. Other niches around the room contained full-length statues. The alcove continued to display an assortment of casts and sculptural copies until the walls of the Hall were rendered flat in the late nineteenth century.

27 *Hercules attacked by the Nemean Lion*

Roman 2nd/3rd century AD
Marble, 880 × 580 × 235
The Ashmolean Museum, Michaelis 38
Visitors of the Ashmolean Museum
Lit. Michaelis 38

This group, formerly in the Arundel Collection, and then in the Pomfret Collection at Easton Neston House, depicts Hercules in the act of fighting the Nemean Lion. The head of Hercules, a restoration which may have been supplied for Arundel or Fermor, was removed in the twentieth century and reinstated in 2001. The figure on the rock behind Hercules, of which the upper part is missing, represents a nymph holding up a victory wreath.

CAT. 27 *Hercules attacked by the Nemean Lion* (Visitors of the Ashmolean Museum)

28–29 *Altar and Inscription*
Altar and Inscription

Marble, 400 × 370 × 320
Marble, 330 × 320 × 250
Roman, early Imperial period
Ashmolean Museum, AN C.3.75; AN C.3.32
Visitors of the Ashmolean Museum
Lit. Chandler C.3.75; C.3.32

These two altars from the Arundel collection were amongst the consignment of inscribed stones transferred to the University of Oxford by John Evelyn in 1667 (Cats.16–18), where they were subsequently recorded by Humphrey Prideaux in *Marmora Oxoniensia* in 1676, and by Richard Chandler in his *Marmora Oxoniensia* of 1763.

The Exedra

30 William Kent (1685–1748)
First design for the exedra, Chiswick, with four figures, c.1733

Pen and wash over pencil, 330 × 515
Devonshire Collection, Chatsworth. Archives 26A, item 24
Lent by the Duke of Devonshire and the Chatsworth
Settlement Trustees
Lit. J. Dixon Hunt, *William Kent, Landscape Garden Designer*,
(London 1987) pp.51–3, 128; John Harris, *The Palladian Revival,
Lord Burlington, His Villa and Garden at Chiswick*, (New Haven
and London 1994) p.234

The idea of a semicircular *exedra* for the display of sculpture
was derived from Italian Renaissance precedents such as
the gardens of the Villa Mattei and Villa d'Este, which in
turn imitated designs from Roman antiquity. This proposal
for the gardens at Chiswick House was rejected and instead
used by Kent for the Temple of British Worthies in the
gardens of Lord Cobham's great house at Stowe (Cat.32).

31 William Kent
View into the exedra at Chiswick, c.1733

Pen and ink and wash over pencil, 290 × 403
Devonshire Collection, Chatsworth. Archives 26A, item 26
Lent by the Duke of Devonshire and the Chatsworth
Settlement Trustees
Lit. J. Dixon Hunt *William Kent, Landscape Garden Designer*,
(London 1987) p.129; John Harris, *The Palladian Revival, Lord
Burlington, His Villa and Garden at Chiswick*, (New Haven and
London 1994) p.236

This design, which was adopted at Chiswick, featured
genuine antique statues standing within an *exedra* of
topiary. According to Daniel Defoe, the statues had been
excavated in the gardens of Hadrian's Villa at Tivoli, and
were denominated as Caesar, Pompey and Cicero. The
idea of carving sculptural niches out of topiary hedges
also comes from Italian Renaissance precedent, and was
observed by John Evelyn at the Villa Medici, (Evelyn,
Diary 1644, Nov. 8) and imitated by the Lord Arundel in
the gardens of Arundel House.

Glimpsed through trees in the background is the column
erected by the 3rd Earl of Burlington carrying a statue of
the Venus de Medici, apparently in emulation of Arundel's
Venus column re-erected at Wilton House (Cat.23).

CAT. 31 *View into the exedra at Chiswick* (Devonshire Collection, Chatsworth)

32 J. H. Gough
The Temple of British Worthies, Stowe, 1910

Photographic print
Stowe School

Kent filled the niches in his curved 'temple' for Stowe,
which reused a design initially drawn up for Chiswick
(Cat.30) with portraits busts of fourteen famous British
'Worthies' flanking one of Mercury, but concealed a joke
at the rear of the structure, a tribute to the virtues of
'Signor Fido,' a dog.

CAT. 32 *The Temple of British Worthies, Stowe, 1910*

33 Unknown hand
Ground Plan of Wilton House as it remained in March 1801

Pen and black ink on paper, mounted on card, with later annotations in red ink and pencil, 490 × 715
Wiltshire Record Office, Wilton House Mss. WHA 2057 H3/21
The Collection of the Earl of Pembroke, Wilton House, Salisbury

When fire destroyed the northern range of Wilton House in 1705, the 8th Earl replaced the Tudor Great Hall with a rectangular 'Grecian' Great Hall entered via an *exedra*-like Vestibule (marked 'k' and 'l' on the plan) which replaced the original Screens Passage. The architect for this work may have been John James.

Antique busts on pedestals were ranged around the Vestibule's curved wall, surrounding a colossal statue of Apollo, formerly in the Giustiniani collection.

This plan (turned through 90 degrees) shows the new sequence of Palladian rooms designed for sculpture at Wilton, which defined the great ceremonial entrance on the ground floor. The gateway into the Great Court was flanked by two Egyptian terms, and the Vestibule was entered via the 'Holbein Porch,' its exterior decorated with sixteenth-century busts in roundels, housing busts of famous military rulers including Hannibal and Miltiades. The Great Stair at the west end of the Great Hall rose to the *piano nobile* and the rooms of parade on the west side of the house, where more of the earl's sculpture was displayed, a progression which culminated with the Double Cube Room in the centre of the state apartments on the south front.

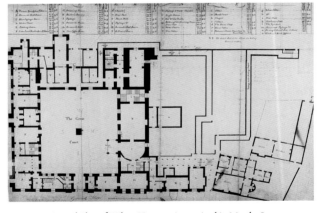

CAT. 33 *Ground Plan of Wilton House as it remained in March 1801*

34 Richard Cowdray
A Description of the Pictures, Statues, Bustoes, Basso-Relievo's and other Curiosities at the Earl of Pembroke's House at Wilton, 1751

Printed booklet in marbled paper covers, 200 × 125
Wiltshire Record Office, Wilton House Mss., WHA 2057 H5/8a
The Collection of the Earl of Pembroke, Wilton House, Salisbury

This, the first printed guide to the sculpture at Wilton, was published by Richard Cowdray, house steward at Wilton in the time of the 9th Earl. The text is dedicated to the earl's friend and Cowdray's mentor Sir Andrew Fountaine, of Narford Hall, who 'pointed out the proper method', but the antiquary George Vertue reckoned that Fontaine was its true author, 'tho the name of a man that has the care of the house and pictures etc. and shews them is put to it . . .' (A. J. K. Esdaile et al. (eds.) *Walpole Society* XXII, Vertue III, 1933–4, p.156.)

Cowdray's text indicates that the largest statues and groups were of necessity placed in the Great Hall, with a bust of the collector-earl presiding from the overmantle. Some of the arrangements were Arundelesque (cf. Cat. 25), with busts placed on top of tomb chests and other sculptures placed on the floor beneath them, and in and beneath the Gallery Wilton's famous suits of armour were arranged, relics of the military prowess of the Pembrokes in the age of chivalry.

35 Matthew Brettingham the Elder
(1699–1769) *attributed to*
Holkham Hall, Proposed plan of the Ground Floor or Rustic Basement, early eighteenth century

Pen, ink and wash, 338 × 522
Holkham Hall Archives, P/M 16
The Earl of Leicester and the Trustees of the Holkham Estate

Thomas Coke, 1st Earl of Leicester and builder of Holkham Hall, was familiar with the 8th Earl's new Palladian rooms for sculpture at Wilton, for he is recorded as a guest in the house in 1741. The semi-circular Vestibule at Wilton, which held eleven busts of emperors and philosophers in niches and a spectacular statue of Apollo from the Giustiniani collection, may anticipate the one devised by Coke and Lord Burlington for the small family entrance on the south front at Holkham. As well as an antique figure of Jupiter, the curving rear wall of the room contains six niches which formerly held casts after famous antique originals in Rome and Florence, including the Apollo

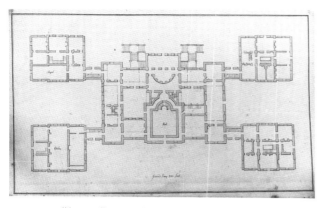

CAT. 35 *Holkham Hall, Proposed plan of the Ground Floor or Rustic Basement*

36 Penry Williams (1798–1885)
Interior of the Amphitheatre or Theatre of the Arts, the Deepdene, 1826

from J. Britton, *Illustrations of the Deepdene, Seat of T. Hope Esqr.*, (1826) p.84.
Watercolour, 210 × 178
Lambeth Archives Department, Minet Library, S3247/185/188
Lit. D. Watkin, *Thomas Hope and the Neo-Classical Ideal*, (London 1968) pp.170–1; G.B. Waywell, *The Lever and Hope Sculptures*, (Berlin 1986) pp.54–5

Although the design of this room was based on the semi-circular plan of the ancient Roman theatre, into the shape of which Hope had carried out research, it was entirely given over to the display of cinerary urns, busts and statues, the latter set in five niches around the curved, *exedra*-like rear wall. The floor was partly composed of a mosaic from Hadrian's Villa.

Belvedere, in situ by *c*.1756 (Holkham Hall Archives, MSS 777, ML C34). Four antique busts of orators and philosophers were placed on brackets on the piers of the dividing wall facing the entrance from the park, and a portrait medallion of another philosopher, 'Carniades,' was fixed to the wall above the chimneypiece.

CAT. 36 *Interior of the Amphitheatre or Theatre of the Arts, the Deepdene, 1826*

The Entrance Hall

37 William Kent
Holkham Hall, Design for the Marble Hall, early eighteenth century

Pen, ink and wash, 335 × 500
Holkham Hall Archives, P/M 3
The Earl of Leicester and the Trustees of the Holkham Estate

For the building of Holkham, Thomas Coke, later 1st Earl of Leicester, and his friend Lord Burlington drew upon material in Palladio and Vitruvius to create a historically accurate Roman house or villa, in which sculpture would play an informing role. By the 1750s the Marble Hall, family entrance and Porter's Hall at Holkham were all ornamented with classical busts and statues and portrait busts of Lord Leicester, in a reference to the precept in Vitruvius which states that the busts of the householder's ancestors should be displayed in the *tablinum* of the Roman house (Vitruvius (1960) VI, 3, vi.).

This, Kent's first design for the great Marble Entrance Hall at Holkham, places a colossal antique statue of Jupiter in the centre of the staircase rising to the Saloon, with niches grouped above it, in the manner of an ancient temple.

38 Matthew Brettingham the Younger (1725–1803)
Rome Account Book for 1747–54

Italian notebook, loosely bound in white vellum, 158 pages written in brown ink
181 × 126
Holkham Hall Archives
The Earl of Leicester and the Trustees of the Holkham Estate
Lit. J. Kenworthy-Browne, 'Matthew Brettingham's Rome Account Book 1747–1754,' *The Walpole Society* XLIX 1983, pp.37–132

This is Matthew Brettingham the Younger's personal Account Book, containing the record of his business dealings in Rome. A number of entries deal with consignments of antique sculpture intended for Holkham Hall, but many more transactions and patrons are also listed, involving engravings, paintings, books, antiquities, and casts for which Brettingham was purchasing new moulds to be made from antique sculpture. Brettingham's activity and enterprise as a dealer who could provide the latest sculptural furnishings for the new Palladian architecture made a significant contribution to the success of his father's architectural practice.

39 Jonathan Richardson, senior (1665–1745) and junior (1694–1771)
An Account of some of the Statues, Bas-reliefs, Drawings and Pictures in Italy &c, with Remarks, London 1722

Printed book, twentieth-century binding in brown buckram, 200 × 130
The Society of Antiquaries of London

Describing the works of art which could be seen by travellers in Holland, France and Italy, this guide was compiled by Jonathan Richardson senior from the letters despatched to him while abroad by his son. Of the Belvedere Garden of the Vatican he wrote:

'Tis a small Square, not quite so large (I believe) as that of Lincoln's Inn. Round it are statues shut up with Doors as in Closets; those of Tyber, and the Nile are in the Middle, two sepulchral Urns are at two of the corners.' (p.275)

Although the text sometimes deteriorates into little more than a list, it provided an invaluable itinerary for those making the Grand Tour, indicating those private collections which were open to visitors, and more importantly, providing value judgements towards the formation of the 'correct' taste, of particular use to would-be connoisseurs, many of whom would have never previously encountered an antique statue.

40 James Gibbs (1682–1754) *attributed to*
Kedleston Hall, Design for an Entrance Hall, 1726

Pen, ink and watercolour, 370 × 515
Kedleston Hall, The Scarsdale Collection (The National Trust, acquired with the aid of a grant from the National Heritage Memorial Fund, 1988)
Lit. L. Harris, (ed.) *Robert Adam and Kedleston, the Making of a Neo-Classical Masterpiece*, (National Trust 1987) pp.16–17

This design probably represents a proposal for the adaptation of the hall of the old house at Kedleston by Smith of Warwick, built *c*.1700 for Sir John Curzon, the 3rd Baronet, and demolished by Nathaniel Curzon, 1st Baron Scarsdale, *c*.1759. The two-storey Entrance Hall filled with sculpture was to be realised in Robert Adam's grandiose designs for the Marble Hall in the new house (see Cat.47), the design and building of which he superintended for Lord Scarsdale from 1760.

41–2 Matthew Brettingham the Elder *attributed to*
Kedleston Hall, Two designs for a Sculpture Hall,
c.1758

Pencil, pen, ink and wash, 190 × 290
Pencil, pen, ink and wash, 318 × 215
Kedleston Hall, The Scarsdale Collection (The National Trust,
acquired with the aid of a grant from the National Heritage
Memorial Fund, 1988)
Lit. J. Kenworthy-Browne, 'Designing around the Statues,
Matthew Brettingham's casts at Kedleston,' in *Apollo* 374,
(April 1993) pp.248–252

Lord Scarsdale had acquired a set of plaster casts of antique
statues from Joseph Wilton in 1757, and more from
Matthew Brettingham the Younger the following year, and
these became the defining feature of his father's designs for
the projected Entrance Hall of the new house. The first of
Brettingham's elevations was closely based on the design
of the Marble Hall or Egyptian Hall which he had built at
Holkham Hall for Thomas Coke, 1st Earl of Leicester
(Cat.37). The second design, with statues standing in niches
placed at dado height between giant columns, was to be
the solution adopted and refined by Robert Adam when
he took over the commission for Nathaniel Curzon's new
house at Kedleston in 1760.

43 Robert Adam (1728–1792) and James
Adam (1732–1794)
Design for the Entrance Hall at Syon House

from *The Works in Architecture*, vol. II, part IV plate I (1779)
Engraving, 510 × 634
By kind permission of Mr Ian Scott

Robert Adam began working at Syon House by the Thames
at Isleworth from 1761, creating a sequence of five new state
rooms within the existing Jacobean House, four of which
were to display sculpture. Adam had been commissioned
to remodel the old house as a classical villa to be used for
lavish entertaining, by the 1st Duke of Northumberland,
who had taken the name and arms of the wife who had
brought him a fabulous inheritance. This is one of four
plates illustrating Syon engraved for Adam by G. B.
Piranesi, conveying the room's overpowering antique
character as a Roman *atrium*, 'consecrated to their
ancestors, and adorned with their images, their arms, their
trophies and other ensigns of military and civil honours.'
(R. Adam 1764, p.5) Significantly, this was the only room
to display genuine Roman portrait statuary, rather than
plaster casts, in a symbolic reference to antique practice.

CAT. 43 *Design for the Entrance Hall at Syon House*

44 Lancelot Brown (1716–1783)
Broadlands House, Plan of the East Front, c.1770

Pen and ink, 317 × 520
Broadlands House Archives
By kind permission of Lord Romsey
Lit. D. Grassinger, *Antike Marmorskulpturen auf Schloss
Broadlands, Corpus Signorum Imperii Romani III, 4,*
(Mainz 1994) pp.34–6

Between 1766–80 Henry Temple, 2nd Viscount Palmerston, employed Lancelot 'Capability' Brown to landscape the park at Broadlands and give the house a new classical façade. Brown produced this proposal for a new East Front and Portico giving directly on to a large hall-cum-sculpture gallery with apses at either end containing niches for Palmerston's Grand Tour sculptures, the bulk of which he had purchased from Gavin Hamilton in Rome in 1764. The rest of the collection would presumably have been displayed in the body of the room, on the marble slab-topped tables bought for the purpose in Rome, and on brackets in the walls. With its Palladian plan-form this room resembles the Sculpture Gallery at Holkham Hall, itself based on Lord Burlington's earlier model of the Saloon at Chiswick House, and Adam's remodelling of the Entrance Hall at Syon House (Cat.43). It was to remain unbuilt, and the sculpture was instead housed in the present Entrance Hall redesigned in 1788–92 by Brown's competent son-in-law, Henry Holland.

45 Madeline Wyndham
Petworth House, the Marble Hall, c.1865

Watercolour, 300 × 490
Petworth House
By kind permission of Lord Egremont
Lit. C. Rowell, *Petworth House, West Sussex,*
(National Trust 1997) pp.16–18, 91

Classical sculpture became a highly important element in the furnishings of the entrance halls of grand country houses in the early eigthteenth century. This view shows the 1st Lord Leconfield as a widower painted by his daughter-in-law in the Marble Hall, formerly the principal entrance to Petworth House, which he had converted to use as a comfortable study. Behind him stands one of the two marble statues, portraying a toga-clad Roman, which had probably occupied niches on the rear wall of the room since the time of the 6th Duke of Somerset (1662–1748), who created the hall and its panelled interior.

46 Sir John Vanbrugh (1664–1726)
Blenheim Palace, Oxfordshire, Elevation of one wall of the Saloon, c.1707

Pasted into folio with inscription, *Drawings, Elevations,
Plans and Details of Blenheim by Sir John Vanbrugh,*
[*Highly Curious*]
Pen, ink and wash on paper, 470 × 495
The Bodleian Library, University of Oxford, MS., Top.
Oxon., a.37*, f.32
Lit. G. Beard, *The Work of John Vanbrugh,* (London 1986) p.121

This, the first idea for the Saloon which Vanbrugh and Hawksmoor proposed, uses giant marble Corinthian columns and five round-headed niches holding ten-foot-high statues personifying the Virtues which Vanbrugh was then trying to obtain in Italy. The same architects produced a comparable scheme articulated by antique statues for the Great Hall at Castle Howard, and schemes featuring painted *trompe l'oeil* statuary and vases at Kings Weston and in the Entrance Hall and Staircase at Easton Neston (further embellished by some of the Arundel Marbles, Cats.26–27). These elements served to add drama and *dignitas* to the experience of passing into the state rooms of a great house. The niches at Blenheim were, instead, eventually covered by the paintings of Louis Laguerre.

CAT. 45 *Petworth House, the Marble Hall,* c.1865 (National Trust Photographic Library/John Hammond)

CAT. 46 *Blenheim Palace, Oxfordshire, Elevation of one wall of the Saloon, c.1707 (The Bodleian Library, University of Oxford)*

47 Adam Office

Design for the Hall and Saloon at Kedleston Hall, Derbyshire, c.1761.

Inscribed *Section of the New Design for Sir Nathaniel Curson Baronet at Kedleston/ now Lord Scarsdale/from North to South*
Pen with grey, pink and yellow washes, 606 × 1293
Sir John Soane's Museum, Adam Vol. 40/3
Lit. L. Harris, *Robert Adam and Kedleston*, (National Trust 1987) pp.58–9; A. A. Tait, *Robert Adam, The Creative Mind: from the sketch to the finished drawing* (Soane Museum 1996) p.19

Kedleston's Entrance Hall, one of the grandest interiors in England, and the circular Saloon on the house's garden front which adjoined it, were designed by Robert Adam to represent the equivalent of the interlinking *'atrium'* and *'vestibulum'* in a Roman palace. Curzon was already buying plaster casts from Italy in 1757–8 to embellish his new house, and these were incorporated into the designs made by the architects who preceded Adam there (Cats.41, 42). Initially, the Marble Hall held only a pair of casts of Apollo and Meleager at the south end, but the Saloon was designated a Sculpture Gallery holding twelve of Curzon's casts. The hall's furnishings were 'Twelve Seats, after the Antique Sarcophagus,' (Cat.66).

CAT. 47 *Design for the Hall and Saloon at Kedleston Hall, Derbyshire, c.1761*

The Long Gallery and the Great Room

48 George Vertue (1680–1725)
Wilton House, View of One End of the Great Room Designed by Inigo Jones, c.1731

in Carlo Gambarini, *A Description of the Earl of Pembroke's Pictures at Wilton*, (Westminster 1731)
Pen and ink and brown wash, 120 × 200
Courtesy of the Lewis Walpole Library, Yale University

This, George Vertue's copy of Gambarini's catalogue to the pictures at Wilton annotated with his sketches, was later owned by Horace Walpole. Vertue was particularly interested in the way sculpture was deployed at Wilton, for between 1725–35 he drew up a detailed 'Plan of the Great Floor of Wilton House' (Bodleian Library, Gough Drawings a1. f.14) indicating the quantities of antique sculpture displayed there. The 'Great Room' or Double Cube Room represented the climax of a sequence of ceremonial rooms of state constructed in Stuart times to accommodate royal visitors, and to this end it was furnished with Van Dyck's huge dynastic portraits of the Pembroke family and of Charles I, augmented by 26 of the highest ranking busts in Wilton's pantheon, of Caesars, emperors, consuls and the goddess Diana.

CAT. 48 *Wilton House, View of One End of the Great Room Designed by Inigo Jones, c.1731*

49 Hugh, Ist Duke of Northumberland (1715–1786)
Copy of a Memorandum, given by Lord Northumberland to Mr. Worsley to be sent to Mr. Hamilton at Naples, June 7th 1765

Pen and ink, 188 × 255
Northumberland Misc. MSS G/1/4
By kind permission of The Duke of Northumberland

In 1764 Horace Walpole observed that 'the gallery [the former Long Gallery of the old house at Syon] is converted into a museum in the style of a columbarium, according to an idea that I proposed to my Lord Northumberland' (G. Jackson Stops, *Country Life* CLXXXVI, 16 April 1992, p.99). The Duke seems to have been enthusiastic about following Walpole's idea literally, for the following year he despatched this memorandum via the hand of Sir Thomas Worsley to Hamilton, the British envoy newly arrived in Naples who was soon to become famous as Sir William Hamilton, the connoisseur, vase collector, and husband of the notorious Emma :

> Lord Northumberland will esteem Himself very particularly obliged to Mr Hamilton if He will purchase for Him any Statues, Vases Tripods or other pieces of Vertu fit to stand in Nitches off 4f 8 in High by 2f 3 in Broad and If I and a half in Deep, of which there are Ten in the Galary at Sion; There are also Four Circular Recesses 18 Inches Diameter by 12 Inches Deep fit for placing any flat Vases or Sepulchral Urns.

Had the duke's plan succeeded then Syon would have housed the first private neo-classical 'museum' of antiquities in England, but within two years decorative paintings and statuettes after the antique had instead been substituted for genuine antiquities (Cat.50), which were probably too difficult to find in the exact sizes needed.

CAT. 50 *Design for the Long Gallery at Syon House*

50 Robert and James Adam
Design for the Long Gallery at Syon House

from *The Works in Architecture*, vol. III, 1822 (reprinted 1980)
plate 2
Engraving, 360 × 460

Adam's drawing for a 'Rock Room' at Kedleston, also executed in the early 1760s (Cat.60), draws on the same architectural precedent of a columbarium, and uses some of the same motifs as are found at Syon. The plate of the Gallery engraved for publication shows the 'landscapes from the antique' and small bronze statues from Mr. Byres in Rome which he substituted for antiquities, but some 'Etruscan' style vases or eighteenth-century replicas were placed in the round recesses above the niches in the Gallery.

51–54 The 2nd Marquess of Rockingham
(1730–1782) *attributed to* and Thomas Bromwich (d.1787)
Lord Rockingham's sketch for the Long Gallery at Wentworth Woodhouse

Pen and ink on paper, 139 × 186

Three designs from Mr. Bromwich for the Long Gallery at Wentworth Woodhouse, fireplace wall

Pencil and green and yellow wash, 164 × 315
Pen and ink and grey and green wash, 120 × 240
Pen and ink and grey wash, 125 × 240
Sheffield City Archives, Wentworth Woodhouse Muniments, WWM.R 185/13-16
The Wentworth Woodhouse Muniments have been accepted in lieu of tax by H. M. Government and temporarily allocated to Sheffield City Council
By kind permission of the Head of Sheffield Leisure Services

CAT. 51 *Sketch for one wall of the Long Gallery at Wentworth Woodhouse, attributed to the 2nd Marquess of Rockingham*

CAT. 52 *One of three designs from Mr Bromwich for the Long Gallery at Wentworth Woodhouse, Fireplace Wall*

The 2nd Marquess of Rockingham, a notable collector of bronzes, coins and medals, bought a number of small decorative marble sculptures during the 1760s, apparently with the intention of furnishing a sculpture gallery at Wentworth Woodhouse. His chosen site was the house's existing Long Gallery on the *piano nobile*, but perhaps because the walls of the room were insufficiently thick to be excavated for niches, he instead commissioned a *trompe l'oeil* scheme in wallpaper from Mr Thomas Bromwich, a fashionable London cabinet and paperhangings maker.

A rough sketch of one wall attributed to Rockingham is shown with the three alternative designs for the western arm of the gallery produced by Bromwich in *c.*1763. Bromwich repeated and enlarged upon Rockingham's chosen formula of sculpture placed upon brackets above dado height, contained by an architectural frame or pediment, producing rococo, Palladian and Renaissance revival versions of the scheme, the latter based upon the newly published antique aedicules of Pompeii and Herculaneum. The scheme seems not to have been carried out.

55 Charles Townley (1737–1805)
Sketch plan of the Sculpture Gallery at Petworth House, 1791

Pen and brown ink, 160 × 100
Inscribed *gallery at Petworth about 16 × 17 feet*
British Museum Central Archive, BM/TP, TY1/22/1, Notebook, 1782–95, 22 fos., f.15, verso
The British Museum, London
Lit. R. A. Guilding, 'The 2nd Earl of Egremont's Sculpture Gallery at Petworth, A plan by Charles Townley,' in *Apollo* CLI (April 2000) pp.27–9

Charles Townley, an indefatigable visitor to other men's collections, recorded the appearance of the 2nd Earl of Egremont's Sculpture Gallery on a visit in 1791, probably made in connection with his work on the Dilettanti Society's publication of antique sculpture belonging to their members. This is the only known plan of the gallery before it was much altered and enlarged by the 3rd Earl to accommodate his modern British sculpture and paintings in the 1820s. The gallery was formed out of an existing open cloister to house the 2nd Earl's Grand Tour sculptures. Its architect was Matthew Brettingham the Elder, who broadly followed the plan of the gallery at Holkham (Fig.4) with niches symmetrically arranged along the rear wall, but threw out the centre of the window wall in a curving bay, which would have flooded the gallery with light.

CAT. 56 *The Sculpture Gallery at Duchess Street*, 1807

56 *The Sculpture Gallery at Duchess Street*, 1807

from *Household Furniture and Interior Decoration* executed from Designs by Thomas Hope (London 1807) (reprinted 1971) pl. 1
Engraving, 285 × 230
By kind permission of Mr Glynn Boyd Harte
Lit D. Watkin, *Thomas Hope and the Neo-Classical Ideal*, (London 1968) pp.101–2; G. B. Waywell, *The Lever and Hope Sculptures*, (Berlin 1986) pp.43–7; D. Watkin and P. Thornton, 'New Light on the Hope mansion in Duchess Street,' *Apollo* (September 1987) pp.162–177

Hope remodelled the interiors of his Duchess Street Mansion between 1709–1804, in order to display his growing collections there, as a public resource and a 'nursery' for modern art. Like his fellow collectors Charles Townley and Sir John Soane, his method was influenced by the writings of the Baron d'Hancarville, in particular his *Recherches* (Cat.82) with its theories on the meaning of ornament in ancient civilisations. The display rooms in the house were arranged to be experienced sequentially, with Egyptian and Indian Rooms representing 'origins,' and the whole representing a 'progress' through the antique canon to the neo-classical shrine of his Flaxman Room.

The Sculpture Gallery was among the most important of the rooms at Duchess Street, presented as the first plate in his publication. The antique sculptures were arranged in symmetrical rows against yellow walls 'left perfectly plain, in order that the background against which are placed the statues, might offer no inferior ornaments or breaks, capable of interfering, through their outline, with the contour of more important works of art.'

57 H. E. Howard
Castle Howard, The Long Gallery, c.1830

Coloured lithograph, 240 × 330
The Castle Howard Collection
By kind permission of the Hon. Simon Howard
Lit. I. Jenkins, 'Seeking the Bubble Reputation,' *Journal of the History of Collections*, 9, 2 (1997), pp.197–200

C. H. Tatham worked for the 5th Earl of Carlisle at Castle Howard from 1801, primarily devising and arranging a Gallery and a Museum for the collections of pictures and sculpture in the uncompleted Palladian West Wing added by his father in the 1750s. The fireplaces in each arm of the Gallery were designed in a monumental Egyptian style, with antique sculpture built into the overmantle. This lithograph shows Tatham's arrangement of pictures, busts, antique tables and the antique bas-relief of Bacchus and Mete set over the fireplace, which the earl had bought at the sale of the private collection of antiquities belonging to Sir William Hamilton at Christie's in 1801.

Bookcases were installed in the window piers in 1827. Here the gallery is seen in informal, family use, in contrast to the bravura statement of John Jackson's painting of *c*.1810 (Cat.58).

58 John Jackson (1778–1831)
Castle Howard, The Long Gallery, c.1810

Oil on canvas, 840 × 965
The Castle Howard Collection
By kind permission of the Hon. Simon Howard

The Long Gallery's main function as a space for display and promenade is reflected in this view with the 5th Earl of Carlisle and his son, which was probably commissioned to mark the completion of C. H. Tatham's work there (the finishing of the North Wing and Octagon was delayed until 1811–12). It also records the Gallery's role as a shrine to the political values of Fox and his party, for a bust of Fox is shown prominently displayed along with antique heads of Roman emperors, both here and in Tatham's published plate (*The Gallery at Castle Howard* (1811) Pl. III). Tatham contrived a dynastic picture-hang with the great portraits of Lord William Howard and his wife Lady Elizabeth, the Elizabethan founders of Carlisle's branch of the Howard family, flanking the arched doorway, which, in combination with the busts, created a 'pantheon' of historical portraits as a backdrop for his patron.

CAT. 57 *Castle Howard, The Long Gallery, c.1830*

CAT. 58 *Castle Howard, The Long Gallery, c.1810*

Piranesi and Antiquarianism

59 Robert Adam
*Sketch for arranging the sculpture at No. 76
Lower Grosvenor Street, London, c.1760*

Inscribed *Sketch of the Manner of placing the Ancient Marbles
under the Room in my Area*
Pen and ink, 196 × 232
Sir John Soane's Museum, Adam Vol. 54/28
Lit. A. A.Tait, *Robert Adam, Drawings and Imagination*,
(Cambridge, 1993) p.83; Tait, *Robert Adam, The Creative Mind:
from the sketch to the finished drawing* (Soane Museum 1996)
p.46

The antique marble collections which he had seen in
Rome, and Piranesi's methods of presentation in particular,
seem to have had a profound effect on the young Robert
Adam. In the year after his return from Rome he set about
expanding his practice with a new house and drawing office
in Lower Grosvenor Street, displaying his collection of urns
and fragments made in Rome, embedded in the area wall
behind the house. In 1764 a small Gallery or 'Casino' was
built behind the house (Cats.83, 84) as a setting to display
marbles and casts bought by James Adam from Rome to
visiting clients. Visitors would have passed through the
courtyard to reach this building: like Piranesi's showrooms
in the Palazzo Tomati in Rome it combined the functions
of sale-room and museum.

60 Robert Adam
*Design for a Grotto or Rock Room,
Wall Elevation, c.1760*

Pen and ink, with pencil underlay, 160 × 203
Kedleston Hall, The Scarsdale Collection (The National Trust,
acquired with the aid of a grant from the National Heritage
Memorial Fund, 1988)
Lit. L. Harris (ed.) *Robert Adam and Kedleston, the Making of
a Neo-Classical Masterpiece* (The National Trust, 1987) p.84

The annotations on this design by Lord Scarsdale indicate
that he considered it suitable for a room beneath the
Greenhouse originally planned by Adam for the first floor
of the south-west Pavilion of the house at Kedleston,
a plan which was later abandoned. The 'S' curves beneath
the dado, based on Roman sarcophagi, were to feature in
Adam's designs for the Long Gallery at Syon House
(Cat.50) where cinerary urns were also included to give
the character of a columbarium. The fashion for collecting
antiquities of this sort, as well as bas-reliefs, altars,
inscribed stones and sarcophagi, was revived during the
late 1760s and 1770s, when antique statues had become
a much rarer and prohibitively expensive commodity.
By 1794 when C. H. Tatham was in Rome attempting to
procure furnishing statuary for his employer Henry
Holland, the market had become so inflated that even the
fabricated urns and vases made fashionable by the publications of Piranesi were scarce (Soane Museum *C H Tatham's
Letters and Sketches from Rome*, p.3, 19 November 1794).

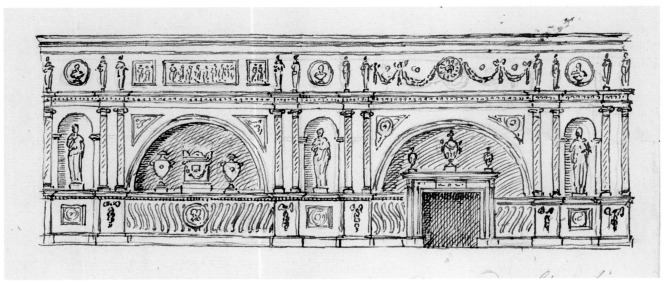

CAT. 60 *Design for a Grotto or Rock Room, Wall Elevation, c.1760* (The National Trust, Kedleston Hall)

CAT. 61 *Design for the Crypt at 12–13 Lincoln's Inn Fields*, 15 June 1808

61   Sir John Soane (1753–1837)
Design for the Crypt at 12–13 Lincoln's Inn Fields, 15 June 1808

Watercolour, 521 × 425
Sir John Soane's Museum, Vol. 83/35
Lit. S. Feinberg Millenson, *Sir John Soane's Museum*,
(Michigan 1987) fig.20, pp.30 and 35

This design, drawn by James Adams, for the 'Crypt', created by Soane in 1808–9, represents the quest for a more literal, archaeologically correct antiquarianism, when compared to Adam's use of the same motifs in his picturesque and decorative schemes for Kedleston Hall and Syon House (Cats.60, 50). One source of inspiration for Soane may have been the sculpture corridor 'Catacombs' at the Earl of Bessborough's villa in Roehampton, Parksted House, designed by William Chambers, which Soane must have seen when he attended the sale of the sculpture there in 1801 (Cat.63). Similar principles dictated the form of the almost contemporary 5th Gallery of Antiquities in the British Museum, arranged by Sir Richard Westmacott and Henry Tresham to receive Charles Townley's marbles in 1806–8.

62   Unknown artist
Hall Chimneypiece at Charles Townley's house in Park Street, n.d.

Pen, ink and wash, 274 × 380
The British Museum, Department of Greek and Roman
Antiquities, Townley Drawings
The British Museum, London
Lit. B. F. Cook, *The Townley Marbles*, (British Museum 1985)
pp. 40–1

In the late 1780s, the Baron D'Hancarville observed of this chimney-piece: *La cheminée de cette chambre est arrangée pour donner l'idée d'un columbarium . . . l'effet est d'autant meilleur qu'il est plus nouveau et moins attendu.* (BM, Greek and Roman Antiquities, 64a, Mss. Cat. Sculptures in Park Street, Westminster, n.d. p.29). It included niches for urns, a bas-relief and a number of inscribed marble tablets (see also Cat.71). It has been identified with the 'Chimney piece composed of antient fragments' which Townley acquired from G. B. Piranesi in 1768. According to Nollekens's pupil and biographer J. T. Smith, sculptural reliefs (the 'Campana reliefs,' Cats.80, 81) and sepulchral urns and inscriptions were also let into the walls of the more private Parlour or Dressing Room on the upper floor of the house (J. T. Smith, *Nollekens and his Times*, 1949, p. 127).

63   James Christie (1773–1831)
A Catalogue of the Capital, Well-Known and Truly Valuable Collection of Antique Statues, Bustoes, Aegyptian and Other Vases, Bas-Reliefs etc . . . the Property of a noble Earl Deceased, 7 April 1801

Printed catalogue, 290 × 220
British Museum, Central Archive, Townley Papers TY 19/129
The British Museum, London

On the death of the 2nd Earl of Bessborough, his collection of sculpture and marble antiquities, displayed in some style at Parksted House, the suburban villa built for him at Roehampton by Sir William Chambers as a 'hommage to antiquity', came on to the market, fetching extremely high prices. The catalogue indicates that many of the sculptures were left undisturbed in their former settings to be viewed to best advantage on the day of sale. Antique vases stood in recessed niches in 'the Catacombs', a groin-vaulted, basement corridor on the garden front of the house, and other pieces were in the Entrance Hall and a number of temples and greenhouses in the grounds. Among those present at the sale who made purchases were Soane himself, Hope, Townley (who was also bidding for his friend Henry Blundell) and an agent acting for the 3rd Earl of Egremont, who bought a group of Pan and Apollo, now in the gallery at Petworth, but failed to secure an antique dog when outbid by both Hope and Townley.

64 Frank Copland (*fl.*1817–20)
Section through the Little Study, 13 Lincoln's Inn Fields, 29 August 1817

Sir John Soane's Museum, Vol. 83/2
Pencil, pen and watercolour, 759 × 555
Lit. S. Feinberg Millenson *Sir John Soane's Museum* (Michigan 1987) p.35, fig.36

This minute room, part corridor and part *antiquarium*, painted Pompeian red, was the site chosen by Soane for the collection of architectural fragments made in Rome by C. H. Tatham for Henry Holland. Some of these originated from the studios of Piranesi and Canova, and in 1816 Soane set them against the walls and above the fireplace of the room, which was flanked by tiers of cineraria in square niches. Soane's models may have included the columbarium-type chimney-piece attributed to Piranesi in Townley's Park Street House (Cat.62).

This drawing, by one of Soane's pupils, recalls the original archaeological records of the collection, drawn by Tatham in Rome, which Soane also owned (*C H Tatham's Letters and Sketches from Rome*).

CAT. 64   *Section through the Little Study, 13 Lincoln's Inn Fields*, 29 August 1817

65 Giovanni Battista Piranesi (1720–1778)
Vasi antico di marmo . . . nel Museo del Cavalier Piranesi

from *Vasi, candelabri, cippi, sarcophagi, tripodi, lucerne, ed ornamenti antichi disegnati ed incisi dal. Cav. Gio. Batt. Piranesi*, Rome 1778, Pl. 65
Engraving, 390 × 260
Inscribed *Al Sig. Cavaliere Enrico Blundell /Amatore delle Belle Arti*
By kind permission of Dr John Martin Robinson

This engraving of an antique vase and cover described as being in the *Museo del Cavalier Piranesi*, has a complimentary dedication to Henry Blundell, whose vast collection of sculpture was housed at his country seat of Ince Blundell in Lancashire. Many of the pieces restored or fabricated by Piranesi out of antique fragments, and illustrated here had already been placed in famous collections throughout Europe, and the painter James Barry described the *Vasi* as a scheme of pure advertisement (J. Scott, *Piranesi*, London 1975, p.244).

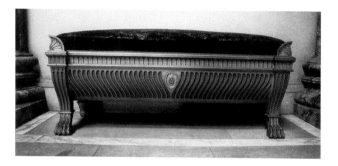

CAT. 66 *Kedleston Hall, Bench, c.1788* (The National Trust, Kedleston Hall)

66 John Linnell (d.1796) from a design by Robert Adam
Kedleston Hall, Bench, c.1788

Painted wood, gesso and velvet, 540 × 500 × 1200
Kedleston Hall, The Scarsdale Collection (The National Trust, acquired with the aid of a grant from the National Heritage Memorial Fund, 1988)
Lit. E. Harris, *The Furniture of Robert Adam*, (London 1963) p.94

A set of 12 painted benches was made for the Marble Hall at Kedleston c.1788. Adam's design was inspired by the sarcophagus or Tomb of Agrippa in the Pantheon, as recorded by Desgodetz. A similar conceit appears in a composition produced by Adam's former drawing tutor in Rome, C.-L. Clérisseau, who included a chest-style sarcophagus serving as a table in his design for a Ruin Room for Santa Trinità dei Monti of c.1766.

67 Robert Adam
Newby Hall, Design for a Pavement for the Sculpture Gallery

Pen, ink and colour wash with pencil, 560 × 965
West Yorkshire Archive Service: Newby Hall Estate Drawings (1/6/23)
Lit. R. Middleton, 'The Sculpture Gallery at Newby Hall,' *AA Files* 13 (Autumn 1986) pp.48–60

William Weddell was a commoner, born into a family which had recently become landed, and elevated by his marriage to the half-sister of the Marchioness of Rockingham to a place in the political circle of her husband, the 2nd Marquess of Rockingham. In 1765 he made a short Grand Tour, buying a consignment of antique sculpture in Rome from the dealer Thomas Jenkins, and by c.1767 he had called in Robert Adam to design a Sculpture Gallery within the part-finished shell of a Gallery adjoining the Dining Room at Newby, begun by John Carr.

Adam produced an interlinking sequence of two rectangular rooms flanking a central circular one, enlivened by apses and niches, the whole smothered with polychrome stucco work featuring *rinceau* patterns and grotesque work. Had the polychrome pavement in this design been executed, the resemblance to Italian Renaissance precedents such as the Villa Madama and Villa Papa Giulio would have been even closer. As Adam's highly fashionable taste, rather than unalloyed antiquarianism, dictated the setting and arrangement of Weddell's Gallery it was almost immediately rated old-fashioned by connoisseurs such as Charles Townley, but it received the highest accolades from Weddell's Yorkshire neighbours.

68 William Belwood (1739–1790)
Newby Hall, Working Drawing for a Pedestal, after a Design by Robert Adam

Pen and ink, 533 × 965
West Yorkshire Archive Service: Newby Hall Estate Drawings (1/6/25)

Bellwood was a York-based architect and builder and there a number of working drawings in his hand amongst the Newby Hall Drawings. Several pedestals in wood and gesso were executed to this typically Adamesque design with ram masks, sphinx and patera decoration.

Charles Townley and the Enlightenment

69–70 Robert Adam

Two Designs for Rooms for Sculpture for Charles Townley, c.1777

One inscribed *Mr. Tow[ ]ey's Room, Portland Place*
Pencil, 155 × 238; 161 × 237
Sir John Soane's Museum, Adam Vol. 27/65, 66
Lit. R. A. Guilding, 'Robert Adam and Charles Townley, the Development of the Top-lit Sculpture Gallery,' *Apollo* CXLIII (March 1996) pp.27–32

By 1770 Townley's most urgent concern was for a house with top-lit rooms to display his sculpture. He briefly considered buying a house in the Adam brothers' ongoing development on the corner of Portland Place and Weymouth Street, for which Robert Adam eagerly provided an unsolicited design, leading to a protracted dispute over payment. Adam proposed a sequence of three interlinked domed rotundas, or an atrium-like Hall with wall-niches, but Townley objected that 'Tho' it was a very compleat family house, it could not suit me, there being no possibility of adding to it the conveniency I wanted, which was a large skylight room on the ground floor,' (BM Central Archives, Townley Papers, TY3/6-11, 1777–9).

71–2 William Chambers (*fl*. 1794)

Charles Townley's House at Park Street, The Entrance Hall, 1794

Charles Townley's House at Park Street, The Dining Room, 1794

Pen and ink with watercolour and touches of gouache, heightened with gum arabic, both 390 × 530
The British Museum, Department of Prints and Drawings, inv. PD 1995-5-6-9/8
The British Museum, London
Lit. I. Jenkins in A. Wilton and I. Bignamini, (eds.) *Grand Tour, the Lure of Italy in the Eighteenth Century*, (Tate Gallery 1997) pp.258–260

As the fame of his collections grew, Townley was gradually drawn into the Establishment, and after about 1796 the house at Park Street was functioning like a rival institution to Montagu House, the first site of the British Museum, with around 600–700 people a year applying to see his collection. These views show Townley's collection when the bulk of it had been bought and arranged to his satisfaction on the ground and first floors of his house in Westminster, and were probably commissioned to show off his latest acquisition, the Discobolus.

The Hall was perhaps the most dramatic space in the house. It was designed as d'Hancarville had recorded, as a columbarium (Cat.62), with a painted ceiling in *trompe l'oeil* representing an upper chamber with an open roof and vases lodged on ledges, and a composite chimneypiece attributed to Piranesi. To the left of the chimera or sphinx mounted on an antique well-head, is a vista of the Dining Room and the Discobolus.

D'Hancarville was consulted over the decoration of the large Dining Room at the back of the house, and the result was a room where symbolism was complex and carefully premeditated. Sculptures whose subjects related to fertility and Bacchanalian rites were brought together here, and even the architectural ornaments were chosen for their relevance to 'the attributes of those Gods, who are supposed by the antients to preside over the festive board.'

73 Joseph Bonomi (1739–1808)

Towneley Hall, Design for a Sculpture Rotunda, c.1783

Watercolour, 508 × 840
Private Collection
Lit. C. Saumarez-Smith, *Eighteenth-Century Decoration, Design and the Domestic Interior in England*, (London 1993) pp.344–5; R. Guilding, 'Robert Adam and Charles Townley, the Development of the Top-lit Sculpture Gallery,' *Apollo* CXLIII (March 1996) pp.27–32

In the 1780s Townley made plans for a large oval rotunda to terminate the new suite of neo-classical rooms which John Carr had executed between 1767–1779 in the south-east wing of his house in Lancashire. In 1783 he paid Bonomi to copy a sketch which he had made 'of the alterations at Towneley for ye marbles.' (See Fig.14, p.12) Bonomi spent part of that year showing tourists around the archaeological sites of Rome, and his design seems to be based on a reconstruction of the Scenic Trinclinium of Hadrian's Villa, demonstrating close knowledge of what remained of this building. The statues were to be informally grouped against the walls, enabling Townley to fulfill his ambition of showing all his sculptures 'assembled together with their different classes,' in order to demonstrate the *arrangement mythologique* recommended by d'Hancarville: one which he had also prescribed for his neighbour Henry Blundell's Rotunda at Ince (BM Central Archive, Townley Papers, TY 6/6, n.d., TY 15/17/4, 1801).

CAT. 71 *Charles Townley's House at Park Street, The Entrance Hall*, 1794
(The British Museum, London)

74 *Charles Townley's Visiting Card*

Inscribed *Mr. TOWNLEY/Park S^t. Westm^r.*
115 × 145
Towneley Hall Art Gallery, Burnley

(See p.56)

75 *Antonio Canova's Visiting Card*

Inscribed *A. CANOVA*
48 × 77
Carmarthenshire Record Office, Cawdor MSS 2/285
By kind permission of the Dowager Countess of Cawdor

(See p.56)

CAT. 72 *Charles Townley's House at Park Street, The Dining Room*, 1794 (The British Museum, London)

76 Charles Townley
*A list of the marbles in Wilton House,
Extracted from the 13th Edition of the* Aedes
Pembrochianae *published in the year 1798,
and observations upon each of the marbles,
written opposite to them in red ink.*

Manuscript notebook, loose leaves sewn into stiff boards
covered in treliss-patterned paper, red and black ink and
pencil, 270 × 170
The British Museum, Central Archive, Townley Papers
TY15/8/1, f.17
The British Museum, London

Townley was an indefatigable recorder of other people's
antiquities, often jealous of those who owned finer pieces
than his own, or scathingly critical of the rest.

This home-made notebook, which contains Townley's
bookplate, has descriptions taken from the *Aedes
Pembrochianae*, George Richardson's popular guidebook
to the sculpture at Wilton House, copied on to the left-
hand page, with Townley's own assessments in red ink
on the facing page. It is shown open at the descriptions of
the twenty-six busts then displayed in the Great Room or
Double Cube Room, for which Townley's comments
typically range from 'modern' to 'coarse and mutilated,'
'ruined' and 'mere defaced rubbish.' Townley was
particularly averse to the common practice of using
'pomice' stone to repolish the surface of a sculpture to
conceal fractures or modern restorations (BM Central
Archive, Townley Papers, TY7/432, 1786). In his summary,
he concluded that only forty-five pieces of sculpture out
of this famous collection which he numbered at a total of
two hundred and seventy-five were of 'sufficient merit to
be admitted into a collection of marbles.'

CAT. 78 *Drawing, Small Torso of a Venus,
rear view* (The British Museum, London)

77 *Small torso of a Venus*

Probably 1st century BC
Marble, h.345
The British Museum, Department of Greek and Roman
Antiquities, GR 1805. 7-3.17, BM cat. sculp. 1580
The British Museum, London

This broken torso from a statuette of a Venus binding
her sandal was purchased by Townley in Rome from the
personal collection of the restorer and sculptor Bartolomeo
Cavaceppi, who used the figure as a model in his studio.
While Townley owned it, it had been restored to stand
upon a wooden pedestal carved to resemble a basin and
drapery, in the attitude of stepping from the bath (Cat.78);
this eighteenth-century pedestal has been replaced by a
modern one.

78 Unknown artist
Drawing, Small Torso of a Venus, rear view

Black chalk, 410 × 245
The British Museum, Department of Greek and Roman
Antiquities, Townley Drawings
The British Museum, London

Townley employed numerous draftsmen and artists, some
of them art students such as Nollekens's biographer J. T.
Smith, to record the pieces in his collection. He was frankly
apprieciative of the various beautiful representations of the
female portrait and nude which he owned, and this torso
(Cat.77) recorded from both back and front in high quality
drawings, was obviously highly prized by him.

79 C. Knight after Henry Howard (1769–1847)
Isis Magna Mater, 1804

Engraving, 300 × 235
Inscribed *From a Bust in the Collection of Charles Townley Esqr.*
Collection of Ruth Guilding

This was Charles Townley's favourite work of sculpture,
purchased in 1772 from the family of Principe Laurenzano
in Naples, which he first identified as Clytie rising from
the Sunflower, and which D'Hancarville categorised as
sepulchral, representing both the individual and her
apotheosis, (Townley later reidentified the work as Isis
Aphrodite or Isis in the Flower of a Lotus). When his house
and collection at Park Street was threatened by the Gordon
Riots in 1780 this was apparently the only one of his
sculptures which he took with him in his flight from the
house, and he used jocosely to call it his 'wife'. The sculpture probably represents a portrait of a Roman lady, and
has been extensively reworked in the eighteenth century.

80 Bas-relief of Aphrodite on a Goose

Roman, 1st-2nd century AD
Terracotta, 308 × 457
The British Museum, Department of Greek and Roman
Antiquities D 508 GR 1805.7-3.348
The British Museum, London
Lit. *A Description of the Ancient Terracottas in the British
Museum*, (London 1810) Pl. XXXV

Townley bought a collection of terracotta bas-reliefs
known as the 'Campana reliefs' from Nollekens in *c*.1783
(BM Central Archives, Townley Papers, TY10/20-21) and
they were displayed set into the walls of his Parlour or
Dressing Room at Park Street. After his death they were
mounted on the walls of the 1st Gallery of Antiquities in
the British Museum by Richard Westmacott and Henry
Tresham in 1806–8 (Cat.81), in symmetrical arrangements
which may have been based upon those devised by
Townley for his house-museum.

81 A Description of the Collection of Ancient Terracottas in the British Museum, (1810)

Gallery of Antiquities, British Museum, North Side of the
First Room
Printed book, 310 × 250
The London Library
Lit. B. Cook, 'The Townley Marbles in Westminster and
Bloomsbury,' *British Museum Yearbook II*, (1977) pp.60–1

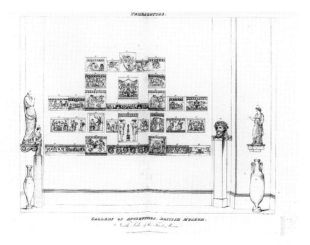

CAT. 81 *Gallery of Antiquities, British Museum, North side of the First Room,
1810*

82 D'Hancarville, (P. F. Hugues called Baron), (1719–1805)
Recherches sur l'Origine, l'Esprit et les Progrès des Arts de la Grèce

3 vols (London 1785–6)
each 300 × 240
Sir John Soane's Museum
Lit. I. Jenkins, in I. Jenkins and K. Sloane, (eds.) *Vases and
Volcanoes*, (British Museum 1996) pp.45–51; D. Watkin,
*Sir John Soane, Enlightenment Thought and the Royal Academy
Lectures*, (Cambridge 1996) pp.262–5

Townley had first met the self-styled Baron d'Hancarville in
Naples in 1768, almost immediately after his publication of
Sir William Hamilton's first Vase Collection had appeared.
During the 1770s, as his reputation as a leading connoisseur
was established, Townley came to recognise d'Hancarville
as both consummate scholar and propagandist, who could
give his collection a prominent place in the art canon of
Europe, the service which he had rendered so successfully
for Hamilton.

In *c*.1778 Townley invited d'Hancarville to undertake the
huge task of making a cross-referenced catalogue of all the
objects in his collection for publication. The task was never
completed, and instead between 1778–1785 d'Hancarville
researched and compiled a much more extensive *chef
d'oeuvre*, mainly at Townley's expense. D'Hancarville
assured his patron that the *Recherches* would stand as a
lasting monument to both their names and give Townley's
marbles a key place in the history of art, '*commme ceux du
comte d'Arundel . . .*' (British Museum, Central Archive,
Townley Papers, TY17/1, n.d.)

The resulting work is both dense and prolix, and
d'Hancarville's arguments and methodology are often
almost impenetrable. Its content was radical in offering an
examination of the religions, literature and imagery of India
and the Far East, for comparison with the art of ancient
Greece. D'Hancarville interpreted the imagery recurrent in
these ancient civilisations as evidence of a common ancient
monotheistic theology, inferring that the origin of all art
was in a religion of sexuality. Townley presented many
copies of the work to his friends, including the collectors
Henry Blundell and Sir Richard Worsley, and its theories
were highly influential for Thomas Hope and Sir John
Soane, as well as providing the methodology for the display
of Townley's sculpture.

The Museum Room

83–4 Robert Adam
Design for a Casino for 76 Lower Grosvenor Street. Sketch of the Niches with Pilasters

Sir John Soane's Museum, Adam Vol. 7/200, 223
Pencil, 242 × 178
Pencil, pen and ink, 319 × 205
Lit A. A.Tait, *Robert Adam, Drawings and Imagination*, (Cambridge 1993) pp.84–7

These sketches record the small 'Casino' or gallery built in 1764 behind the Adam brothers' new house and Drawing office off Upper Grosvenor Street, to display antiquities bought back from Rome by James Adam for sale. It was conceived as a gorgeous museum anticipating the Sculpture Gallery devised at Newby Hall, with niches framed by panels and pilasters decorated with *rinceau* patterns, acting as a foil to display the sculpture to its best advantage.

85 Edward Francis Burney (1760–1848)
The Antique Room at old Somerset House, 1779

Pen and coloured wash, on paper, 337 × 489
The Royal Academy of Arts

Like their architect contemporaries, a number of practising neo-classical sculptors followed antiquarian practices in the late nineteenth and early twentieth centuries, collecting pieces of antique sculpture to furnish private museums in their studios, which could also serve as exemplars or study-pieces for their work. Both Canova and Piranesi kept private museums which served as libraries of antique design and style, and Nollekens also collected both marbles and terracottas, although these were usually for restoration and sale. These collections seem not to have been recorded, but must have resembled the jumbled assemblage of casts and copies made for the art students of the Royal Academy and illustrated here.

86 Eliza Westmacott (b.1802)
Sir Richard Westmacott in his Study at 14 South Audley Street, c.1840–56

Watercolour over pencil, 302 × 451
Henry Moore Institute, Leeds, WES/MISC D28
Lit. N. Penny, 'The Sculpture of Sir Richard Westmacott,' in *Apollo* 102 (August 1975) pp.120–7; M. Buscoe, *Sir Richard Westmacott, Sculptor*, (Cambridge 1994) p.20

Westmacott was an extraordinarily successful figure in early nineteenth-century England. Between c.1800–30 he supplied neo-classical works of sculpture for Holkham Hall, Petworth House, Woburn Abbey and Chatsworth House, many of which were displayed in juxtaposition with antique marbles. He also built up an influential role as an advisor and curator of collections of ancient marbles, at Chatsworth, at Wilton Abbey and in the new Sculpture Galleries of the British Museum, where he acted as an advisor until the time of his death. He escorted his friend Antonio Canova on his visit to England in 1815, mixed on easy terms with many of his aristocratic patrons, and was knighted in 1837.

He owned a notable collection of medals, Etruscan vases, bronzes, marbles, prints and books, and this view, painted by his daughter, shows the artist in cultivated old age, surrounded by a museum-like ensemble of these objects.

CAT. 85 *The Antique Room at old Somerset House*, 1779
(Royal Academy of the Arts, London)

CAT. 86 *Sir Richard Westmacott in his Study at 14 South Audley Street*, c.1840–56

87 Penry Williams
The Sculpture Gallery, the Deepdene, 1826

from J. Britton, *Illustrations of the Deepdene, Seat of T. Hope Esqr.*, (1826) p.87
Watercolour, 235 × 179
Lambeth Archives Department, Minet Library, S3247/185/188
Lit. D. Watkin, *Thomas Hope and the Neo-Classical Ideal*, London 1968, p.171; G. B. Waywell, *The Lever and Hope Sculptures*, Berlin, 1986, pp.52–4

The Deepdene, the house purchased by Hope in 1807, and subsequently much altered and enlarged, offered the chance to experiment with new styles and a larger space in which to develop his ideas. The sculptures were installed here between 1822–7, new pieces of sculpture were bought, and much of the sculpture at Duchess Street was moved here, although a nucleus remained behind. The Sculpture Gallery was lighted by a central fanlight and through the open side wall which its shared with a greenhouse, communicating with the Library at one end and terminating in an *exedra* at the other, but its symmetrical arrangement with two rows of sculpture lining the walls is very similar to that of the gallery at Duchess Street (Cat.56), although here, antique sculptures were exhibited alongside modern copies.

88–95 *Sculpture fragments from the 6th Duke of Devonshire's Museum at Chatsworth House*

Two draped figures, head of bearded faun, foot of a griffin, four hands
Marble, dates between 5th century BC and 1st century AD
Devonshire Collection, Chatsworth
Lent by the Duke of Devonshire and the Chatsworth Settlement Trustees
Lit. D. Boschung, H. von Hesberg, A. Linfert, *Die antiken Skulpturen in Chatsworth, Monumenta Artis Romanae XXVI*, (Mainz, 1997) pp.11–16; R. A. Guilding 'Play a Duke's Game of Marbles', *Country Life* (June 7 2001) pp.162–165

During the 1820s and 30s the 6th Duke of Devonshire created his own *antiquarium* in a small room in the western entrance at Chatsworth (Fig.21). The room was gradually filled with a collection of souvenirs and antique fragments amassed by the duke and his friends and family, but the nucleus of the collection was a tiny headless female torso, found in the ruins of the Emperor Hadrian's Villa and given to him by the sculptor Antonio Canova in 1819. When Canova died three years later, the duke hurriedly purchased memorials of him from his brother in the form of 'poor Canova's favourite bits of ancient marble,' the antique hands and other fragments which had formed a private 'museum' in his studio, and served as models for his work.

96 W. G. S. Cavendish, 6th Duke of Devonshire, (1790–1858)
Handbook to Chatsworth and Hardwick, 1845

220 × 190
Devonshire Collection, Chatsworth
Lent by the Duke of Devonshire and the Chatsworth Settlement Trustees
Lit. D. Cavendish, Duchess of Devonshire, *The House, A Portrait of Chatsworth*, (London 1982) pp.29–30

The 6th Duke of Devonshire recorded the numerous improvements which he made to the house and grounds at Chatsworth in his privately published *Handbook*, written in the form of a letter to his eldest sister, Harriet. After listing the contents of his museum of fragments he concluded, 'Many of these are exceedingly interesting to me, and chiefly those belonging to Canova' (*Handbook* p.156).

97–8 *A Description of the Collection of Ancient Marbles in the British Museum, Part 2, 1815* The Townley Gallery, Room III, East and West Sides

Engravings, each 255 × 305
Collection of Ruth Guilding
Lit. B. Cook, 'The Townley Marbles in Westminster and Bloomsbury,' *British Museum Yearbook II*, (1977) pp.59–66

Townley bequeathed his collection to the British Museum in 1802, and two years later, new galleries designed by George Saunders were begun at Montagu House to accommodate it. Shortly before his death Townley changed his will in favour of his heirs, and the Museum was instead obliged to purchase the marbles in 1805. The sculptures were eventually arranged in their new top-lit galleries by Richard Westmacott and Henry Tresham between 1806–8. Room III contained a symmetrical arrangement of statues, busts and reliefs, shown against walls which were painted in plain distemper.

Antiquity versus Neo-Classicism

99   Charles Townley
Sketch plan for a Temple for the Conservatory at Woburn House, c.1802

Pen, ink and wash over pencil, 200 × 328
The British Museum Central Archive, BM TP, TY14/3/4
The British Museum, London
Lit. E. Angelicoussis, *The Woburn Abbey Collection of Classical Antiquities, Monumenta Artis Romanae,* (Mainz 1992) pp.16–18

When Francis Russell, 5th Duke of Bedford, died suddenly from a tennis injury in 1802, Henry Holland was engaged in erecting a 'Temple of Liberty' for him at one end of the Conservatory-cum-Gallery at Woburn. Holland had built this structure ten years earlier, and by now it housed the Lante vase purchased by the duke from Lord Cawdor's sale in 1800 and several statues, including a full-size copy of the Apollo Belvedere, as well as many plants. The Temple's inner chamber was to enshrine 'Roman' portrait-busts of Charles James Fox and the 5th Duke, and more busts of his friends and supporters were to stand in an outer chamber, all of them commissioned from Joseph Nollekens. The newly-created 6th Duke (1766–1839) considered replacing his brother's bust with a more ostentatious portrait statue by Canova, but at the same time he directed Holland to consult the collector Charles Townley over the proper Greek form and 'classical propriety' of adapting his brother's scheme to this purpose. This, the more finished of two alternative plans of the Temple sketched by Townley, features the outer 'Pronaos' and the inner 'Cella Libertatis' built by Holland. Altars, fountains or furniture were proposed to be placed in front of the temple 'calculated to give the effect of an ancients temple adapted for a modern purpose' (British Museum, Central Archive, Townley Papers TY7/963, 18 April 1802).

CAT. 100   *Woburn House, The Sculpture Gallery, c.1816*

100   Sir Richard Westmacott (1775–1856)
Woburn House, The Sculpture Gallery, c.1816

from Album entitled *Sketches by Sir Richard Westmacott*
Ink and watercolour, 220 × 330
Henry Moore Institute, Leeds, WES/A/S2
Lit. M. Buscoe, *Sir Richard Westmacott, Sculptor,* (Cambridge 1994) p.118–20

In c.1816 when Jeffry Wyattville was adding a corresponding temple to the opposite end of the Conservatory-Gallery at Woburn for the 6th Duke of Bedford, to house Canova's group of the Three Graces, Richard Westmacott was commissioned to supply reliefs to decorate the exterior of the two buildings. The symbolic content of this work was chosen to articulate the meaning of the structures inside – the façade outside the Temple of the Graces was appropriately decorated with putti holding garlands, after those found on antique sarcophagi; on that of the Temple of Liberty, allegorical reliefs depicted putti enacting the development of civilisation.

101   Unknown artist
Woburn House, the Sculpture Gallery, undated

Pencil, 190 × 275
Collection of Ruth Guilding
Lit. E. Angelicoussis, *The Woburn Abbey Collection of Classical Antiquities, Monumenta Artis Romanae,* (Mainz 1992), pp.29, 36–9; M. Buscoe *Sir Richard Westmacott, Sculptor,* (Cambridge 1994) pp.118–20; J. Kenworthy-Browne, 'The Sculpture Gallery at Woburn Abbey and the Architecture of the Temple of the Graces,' in *The Three Graces, Antonio Canova,* (National Gallery of Scotland 1995) pp.61–71

By 1814 the 6th Duke of Bedford had begun collecting antique sculpture and the transformation from Conservatory to Gallery was in full progress at Woburn. This sketch looking down the vista towards the Temple of Liberty, shows the Gallery as it appeared in the 1830s, and may be may be based on a view made for P. F. Robinson's *Vitruvius Britannicus, The History of Woburn Abbey,* (1833–44). It shows the gallery crammed with the marbles amassed by the 6th Duke and his son, Lord William Russell (1790–1846), a mixture of antiquities and a smaller proportion of neo-classical works including bas-reliefs commissioned from Bertel Thorwaldsen, Richard Westmacott and Francis Chantrey set into the walls. The resulting ensemble was comparable to that of the Galleria Chiaramonti in Rome, the gallery of antiquities arranged by Canova in the Vatican in 1805, a similarity which may have been due to Canova's involvement, for he had visited Woburn with Westmacott in 1815. By 1822 the duke was to opine that, 'I should like to have two Sculpture Galleries, one for antiques, and one for modern Sculpture, but I must content myself with what I have got and "dream the rest" . . .'

102 Unknown artist
Chatsworth House, the Sculpture Gallery, early–mid nineteenth century

Pencil, grey washes and white heightening, 510 × 685
Devonshire Collection, Chatsworth
Lent by the Duke of Devonshire and the Chatsworth Settlement Trustees

Although the 6th Duke of Devonshire collected many antiquities, he believed that antique sculptures of the highest quality were no longer obtainable by the 1820s; the great Sculpture Gallery which he built at Chatsworth was instead filled with rare specimen marble pedestals and fine neo-classical sculpture. Jeffrey Wyattville was his chosen architect for this task, having recently enlarged the Gallery at Woburn Abbey and Richard Westmacott presided over its internal arrangement. The design was finalised after the duke's return from his first visit to Rome in 1823, and it was completed in 1833.

103 B. W. Bentley
Chatsworth, the Sculpture Gallery, 1876

Black and white photograph in album, 273 × 375
Devonshire Collection, Chatsworth
Lent by the Duke of Devonshire and the Chatsworth Settlement Trustees

The duke depended entirely on Sir Richard Westmacott to arrange his new Gallery in 1833. It had been conceived as a 'hommage to Canova,' the duke's dead friend and Westmacott's one-time mentor and master, and the bulk of the sculpture was placed in two symmetrically-arranged rows against the walls, with pieces by Canova, his Madame Mere and Endymion, given the most prominent positions nearer the centre of the gallery. Some of Canova's tools together with a cast of his hand were placed in a wall-mounted glass case, and Canova's portrait bust of himself stood opposite the duke's on the end wall of the room.

CAT. 104 *Petworth House, the North Gallery, c.1865* (National Trust Photographic Library/John Hammond)

104 Madeline Wyndham
Petworth House, the North Gallery, c.1865

Watercolour and gouache, 335 × 415
Petworth House
By kind permission of Lord Egremont
Lit. C. Rowell, *Petworth House* (National Trust, 1997) pp.35–7

This view shows the central corridor of the North Gallery at Petworth, the first of two extensions added by the 3rd Earl of Egremont in 1824–5 and c.1827 to accommodate his growing collections of neo-classical works by British sculptors and contemporary British paintings. Turner's view of the Gallery of c.1827 shows the walls painted white (Cat.108), but by the time that this view was made they had been coloured a deep red, comparable to that proposed by Crace for the Gallery at Chatsworth (Cat.111). The 3rd Earl made a point of buying 'only the artistic productions of his own time,' and he advocated mixing modern sculpture with antiquities in the Gallery at Petworth both to advertise the prowess of British artists and to provide exemplars to improve their style, an arrangement which he advocated for the British Museum in 1832.

105 *Osborne House, Three photographic views of the Marble Corridor, early twentieth century*

Postcard, 90 × 140
Collection of Ruth Guilding

Queen Victoria and her husband Prince Albert, the Prince Consort, began building Osborne House in the 1840s as a private villa-palace on the Isle of Wight for themselves and their family, using the master builder Thomas Cubitt. It was also a place where the Prince Consort could try out his experimental and innovative approaches to interior decoration, and build up a collection of art which exhibited his own personal taste, the taste in which he was instructing his young wife.

In emulation of the neo-Italianate 'private' royal houses created by the architect Schinkel during the 1820s and 30s for the Prussian King Friedrich Wilhelm III and his two sons (the transformation of the Schloss Glienecke for Prince Karl, and the innovative remodelling of the Charlottenhof in the park at Sans Souci at Potsdam), Prince Albert was to employ his own German art adviser, Ludwig Gruner, to purchase works of art and advise on the designs for Osborne. Gruner in turn brought in the Berlin decorative painter Müller who had worked at the Charlottenhof, and placed commissions with some of the sculptors whose work was also featured there.

The Marble Corridor provided a link between the private Pavilion Wing and the adjoining Household Wing, connecting the Audience Chamber and Council Room (where the Queen's Privy Council met several times a year) with the formal entertainment and dining suite in the Pavilion. As a processional route, it was decorated with gilding and elaborate polychrome arabesques after Raphael, benches in the neo-Grec taste and plaster reliefs modelled after the Parthenon frieze. The works of sculpture displayed here comprised a few antiquities, more 'ideal' contemporary works which the royal couple exchanged as presents, many with self-consciously 'romantic' subjects, and a 'library' of reduced size bronze copies of the most famous pieces in the classical canon. The house also held portrait sculptures of Victoria and Albert by John Gibson and Emil Wolf respectively, she in a classical tunic with a laurel crown and he in Roman armour. The Corridor's decoration was not finished until the 1860s, and might have been still more elaborate had not the Prince Consort died prematurely in 1861.

CAT. 107 *Osborne House, The Marble Corridor*, 1852 (Royal Collection © 2000 Her Majesty the Queen)

106 Joseph Thürmer (1789–1833) and Johann Gottfried Gutensohn (1792–c.1844)
Villa Madama, General Section of the Loggia

from Ludwig Gruner, *Fresco Decorations and Stuccoes of Churches and Palaces in Italy during the Fifteenth and Sixteenth Centuries*, (second edition, London 1854) Pl.7
Chromolithograph, 410 × 535
Collection of Ruth Guilding

Gruner began working in England for the Prince Consort as a scholar and designer from about 1844. His first task was to publish *Fresco Decorations and Stuccoes of Churches and Palaces in Italy during the Fifteenth and Sixteenth Centuries* (1844) (expanded from an original edition by J. G. Gutensohn), dedicated to the Prince Consort and his fellow members of the Royal Fine Arts Commission, to provide the Commission with an illustrated reference text on Italian decorative painting. Almost simultaneously a number of the design motifs illustrated in this work were adopted for the decoration of the State rooms and public areas at Osborne House.

107 James Roberts (c.1800–67)
Osborne House, The Marble Corridor, 1852

Watercolour, 260 × 365
Royal Collection, RL 23463 DM 4636
Lent by Her Majesty the Queen
Lit. Delia Millar, *The Victorian Watercolours in the Collection of Her Majesty The Queen*, (1995), p.742

At the junction in the Marble Corridor at Osborne where visiting dignitaries would turn off to enter the Audience and Council Chambers, a hiatus was created by the curtained niche coloured blue and gold enshrining the finest antique work in the collection, a Marine Venus or Venus Anadyomene purchased by Gruner at the Stowe Sale in 1848. The design of the niche was closely based upon sections and elevations of the Loggia of the Villa Madama in Gruner's *Fresco Decorations* (Pls.7–13, Cat.106) and other sources in the same work may have provided references for the elaborately patterned mosaic-effect pavements in the Corridor, created from tiles commissioned from Minton.

Romanticism and Marble Mania

108–9 J. M. W. Turner (1775–1851)
Petworth House, The North Gallery from the North Bay: Owen's Portrait of Mrs Robinson hanging to the left of Flaxman's 'St Michael overcoming Satan', c.1830
Petworth House, The North Gallery at Night: Figures contemplating Flaxman's statue 'St Michael overcoming Satan', 1827

Watercolour and gouache on paper, 138 × 189
Pencil, watercolour and gouache on paper, 141 × 192
Tate, D22675, D22687
Bequeathed by the artist, 1856

The 3rd Earl of Egremont was a generous patron of British artists, and Turner was a frequent guest in his house, keeping a studio on an upper floor and making numerous records of its interiors in the form of watercolour sketches. These watercolour sketches show the last and largest bay of the North Gallery, which accommodated the sculptures commissioned by the earl from John Flaxman, and most notably his subject taken from Milton, 'St Michael subduing Satan.' The earl

CAT. 109 *Petworth House, The North Gallery at Night*, 1827
(© Tate, London 2001)

patriotically maintained that Flaxman was the superior exponent of the pure Grecian style, when many of his peers were 'showering commissions on Canova.' On the sculpture's pedestal, he caused an inscription to be cut which stated that the work 'was hardly surpassed by the most celebrated productions of ancient times, and certainly by none of his own.'

CAT. 108 *Petworth House, The North Gallery from the North Bay*, c.1830 (© Tate, London 2001)

CAT. 110 *Petworth House, the Carved Room, c.1865* (National Trust Photographic Library/John Hammond)

110 Madeline Wyndham
Petworth House, the Carved Room, c.1865

Gouache, 400 × 460
Petworth House
By kind permission of Lord Egremont
Lit. C. Rowell, *Petworth House* (National Trust, 1993) pp.16–18;
A. Howkins, 'J. M. W. Turner at Petworth: Agricultural
Improvement and the Politics of landscape,' in: J. Barrell (ed.)
*Painting and the Politics of Culture – New Essays on British Art
1700–1850*, (Oxford and New York 1992) pp.240–249

The 3rd Earl of Egremont remodelled this room in the
1820s, combining historic and family portraits, Chinese
porcelain and carvings by Grinling Gibbons and others
with landscapes by J. M. W. Turner and classical portrait
busts from his father's collection displayed on tables,
pedestals and in bracketed niches. This complex but
powerful dynastic ensemble mingled ancestor worship
with the dignification of property rights, using classical
sculpture and portrait painting in much the same way as
they had been used more than a century earlier in the
Double Cube Room at Wilton House (Cat.48). The room
was devised as a large Dining Room and continued to be
used for this purpose for part of the last century.

111 J. D. Crace (1838–1919)
Chatsworth House, the Sculpture Gallery, 1893

Watercolour, 508 × 685
Devonshire Collection, Chatsworth
Lent by the Duke of Devonshire and the Chatsworth
Settlement Trustees

This proposal from the decorating firm of Crace was made
for 'Harty-Tarty,' the 8th Duke of Devonshire (1833–1908),
a politician who spent much of his time at Devonshire
House in London, but opened Chatsworth for splendid
house-parties in the winter. Crace proposed a 'Pompeian'
colour scheme of terracotta-pink,with a Greek key frieze
to be painted over the Sculpture Gallery's walls of plain
Derbyshire stone. If executed, this scheme would have
transformed the space with a warm colour-scheme in
pleasing contrast to that of Wyattville's orangery beyond,
where at night, powerful lamps lit up more neo-classical
sculpture and tazzas displayed against the foliage of
blossoming orange trees.

The lions in this view, made for the 6th Duke in the
year after Canova's death, are exact copies of those which
Canova had sculpted for his monument to Pope Clement
XIII in St Peter's Church in Rome.

112 James Wyatt (1746–1813), with annotations
by the 11th Earl of Pembroke
Wilton House Notebook, c.1806

Pen, ink, and pencil, notebook with marbled board covers,
195 × 160
Wiltshire Record Office, Wilton House Mss. WHA 2057 H1/8
The Collection of the Earl of Pembroke, Wilton House,
Salisbury

In 1801, in a fit of 'Gothick' enthusiasm, the 11th Earl of
Pembroke bought in James Wyatt, who was simultaneously
working at Fonthill Abbey and at Ashridge, to encase
Wilton House within and without in a Gothic skin which
would advertise its monastic origins. The bulk of the vast
collection of ancient sculpture displayed throughout the
house and grounds since the late seventeenth century
(Cats.22, 23, 24) was to be relocated in Gothic cloisters
encircling Wilton's central court. Wyatt's working
notebooks (cf. WHA 2057 H1/10, *c.*1801) record the
overloaded sculptural compositions composed of busts
on brackets or standing with smaller figures and vases on
top of sarcophagi which were plotted out for every bay in
the cloisters, and the pedestals concealing cast iron stoves,
designed for the finest statues. The earl took an intense
personal interest in the work, and Wyatt's notes were
frequently annotated or overwritten by him. Wyatt worked
on the scheme in a dilatory fashion for almost a decade
until the exasperated earl dismissed him in 1810.

CAT. 111 *Chatsworth House, the Sculpture Gallery*, 1893 (Devonshire Collection, Chatsworth)

113 Sir Richard Westmacott *attributed to*
Wilton House, Design for a Shakespeare Niche,
c.1812–1826

Pen, ink, pencil and coloured wash on card, 250 × 308
Wiltshire Record Office, Wilton House Mss. WHA 2057
H3/18, pt. 2
The Collection of the Earl of Pembroke, Wilton House,
Salisbury

When Wyatt was dismissed from Wilton in 1810, Richard
Westmacott took on a role of considerable responsibility
in his place, supervising the arrangement of the huge
sculpture collection in the partially completed Gothic
cloisters. From its inception the new plan for Wilton was
to make a 'romantic' interior where sculpture would be
displayed in combination with a plethora of symbolic
objects and architecture signifying the rich historical legacy
of the Pembroke family. Westmacott had already supplied
eight figures of historical 'founders' for Gothic niches in the
Staircase Hall at Ashridge Park in *c.*1814, and at Wilton he
sketched a statuette of Henry VIII based on Holbein's
portraits, and the design shown here for Scheemaker's
statue of Shakespeare (see Fig.19, p.15). The statue was to
be displayed in a room behind the Holbein Porch (which
had been dismantled and removed from the Entrance
Court in *c.*1812, and was re-erected in a new site in the
gardens *c.*1819–26), flanked by two carved and gilt
salamactic columns, and two bracket shelfs carrying
busts, probably representing portraits of the Pembroke
family. Westmacott's new room was apparently erected
at the back of the porch, but it no longer exists and this
scheme may not have been fully carried out.

114 Unknown Artist
Arbury Hall, the Gothic Dining Room,
or Front Hall, c.1779

Inscribed *Hall of Arbury*
Pencil and wash, 267 × 335
By kind permission of Mr Charles Hind

From 1748–75 a programme of gothicisation was carried
out at Arbury Hall by Sir Roger Newdigate, 5th Baronet
(1719–1806), to commemorate the house's monastic
origins. Newdigate was a distinguished dilettanti, a patron
of Piranesi (from whom he acquired the Newdigate
Candelabra now in the Ashmolean Museum) and a
collector of books and prints, who made two Grand
Tours in Italy, in 1739–40 and 1774–5.

From 1771 Henry Keene was employed to work on the
'Front Hall' at Arbury, an enclosed Gothic portico on the
south front which formed the aisle of the Dining Room,
and the main room with its fan-vaulted ceiling was finished

in 1779. Newdigate was keenly interested in the display of
works of art, and placed plaster casts of famous sculptures
in the niches in this room. The Dancing Faun after the
famous original in the Tribuna of the Uffizi is displayed on
the end wall, the Tribuna Apollino is on the side wall and a
group of Cupid and Psyche modelled from the one in the
Capitoline Museum is placed above the tomb-like canopy
of the fireplace arch.

115 Anne Salvin
Mamhead, the Sculpture Corridor

Pencil and wash, 340 × 235
RIBA Drawings Collection, PB 96 (11, 6)
Royal Institute of British Architects, London
Lit. J. Allibone, *Anthony Salvin, Pioneer of Gothic Revival
Architecture*, (Cambridge 1988) pp.23–29

Anthony Salvin built Mamhead in Devon in the Tudor
style in *c.*1827–35 for Robert William Newman, a prosper-
ous businessman with a company trading in Portugal and
Newfoundland. The Gallery, in a late Perpendicular Gothic
style, was peopled with paired statues carved by Charles
Raymond Smith representing Lord and Lady Daubeny,

CAT. 115 *Mamhead, the Sculpture Corridor* (Royal Institute of British
Architects, London)

Henry VII and Elizabeth of York, Henry VIII and Lady
Jane Seymour, Queen Elizabeth and Sir Walter Raleigh,
and Cardinal Wolsey and an unidentified bishop, all
personalities of the apparent date of the house, creating
a spurious sculptural ancestry akin to the more genuine
associations evoked by Westmacott at Wilton (Cat.113).
The sculptures were removed and sold at auction in 1985.

116 *Pedestal, Roman*

2nd century AD, restored in the eighteenth century
Marble, 810 × 460, l. of one side of top, 390
British Museum GR 1805.7-3.221, Cat. sculp 2510
British Museum, Department of Greek and Roman Antiquities
The British Museum, London

Tripod base of a candelabrum mounted on three paw feet,
decorated with a tripod, a griffin and a raven turned
towards a laurel-tree, all figures associated with the
god Apollo.

This piece, bought out of a Roman collection, was in the
possession of Charles Townley by 1773. Townley and his
fellow collector Lyde Browne were particularly scathing
about the heavily restored elaborate candelabra and tripods
sold from the studio workshop of Piranesi which they
dubbed *pasticcios*, (BM Central Archive, Townley Papers,
TY7/1497, 1776; TY15/1/1, 1783). During the 1770s Townley
set about purging his collection of these 'fakes', substituting
antique pedestals such as this one, or altars and well-heads
as pedestals for his sculpture, following the latest practices
adopted in the new sculpture galleries of the Museo Pio
Clementino in Rome.

117 R. Ackerman (1781–1850), after William Westall
The Arundel Marbles in the Sculpture Gallery in the Old Schools, Oxford, 1813

from R. Ackerman, *The History of Oxford*, (1814)
Coloured lithograph, 295 × 355
Collection of Ruth Guilding
Lit. M. Vickers, 'The Changing face of Henry VIII,' *Country Life*,
(April 24 1980) pp.1248–1249

For more than a century after their arrival in Oxford in 1755,
the Arundel or Pomfret Marbles, bought by the Dowager
Duchess of Pomfret out of the house and gardens at Easton
Neston (Cats.3, 4, 11, 12, 27), languished in comparative
obscurity in the the University's Old Schools on the ground
floor of the Bodleian Library, until their transferral in the
1870s and 80s to Cockerell's new University Galleries, the
present Ashmolean Museum.

At the time of their removal the restorations made for Sir
William Fermor by Giovanni Battista Guelfi were removed.

118 Unknown pupil of Sir John Soane
The Dome, 12–13 Lincoln's Inn Fields, c.1812–13

Watercolour, 698 × 501
Sir John Soane's Museum Vol. 83/13

Soane bought sculpture for its associations, its novelty,
provenance, and for the clues which it offered to his
continuing study of the history of ancient civilisations.
He owned a vast collection of Greek and Roman marbles,
more than two-thirds of which were fragmentary,
decorative or architectural, together with Egyptian and
Renaissance works, neo-classical pieces and plaster casts.

The lanterned Dome or Tribune was the upper stage of
the centre-piece of his house, standing above the Museum
and Crypt (Cat.61). The Venus is seen here against a
backdrop of miscellaneous architectural and sculptural
pieces. By c.1812–13 his four statues of the Apollo Belvedere,
the Venus de Medici, the Ephesian Diana and the Asclepius
stood around the edges of the display.

119 James Stephanoff (c.1788–1874)
The Connoisseur, 1817

Watercolour, 510 × 700
Private Collection
Lit. I. Jenkins, 'Stephanoff and the British Museum,' *Apollo*
(March 1985) pp.174–181; I. Jenkins, *Archaeology and Aesthetes
in the Sculpture Galleries of the British Museum 1800–1939*,
(British Museum 1992) pl. IX

James Stephanoff, who was amongst the students and
artists employed by Townley to record his collection,
produced a series of six paintings relating to the exhibitions
of Greek and Roman antiquities and associated material
at the British Museum, which were exhibited between
1817–45. This view (see Fig.20, p.17) shows a connoisseur
seated at a desk in a room filled with objects almost entirely
drawn from the collections of Charles Townley and Sir
William Hamilton, here reassembled into an imaginative
and decorative synthesis. Hamilton's 'Etruscan' painted
vases are distributed amongst marble antiquities, bronzes,
terracottas and the contents of a coin cabinet, with an
open folder of prints close by. A dog gazes through a
doorway flanked by Townley's Caryatid and Venus, against
whose legs a fragment of the Parthenon frieze is casually
propped. Among the objects on the connoisseur's desk is
Townley's small marble Torso (Cat.77).

CAT. 74 *Charles Townley's Visiting Card* (Towneley Hall Art Gallery, Burnley)

CAT. 75 *Antonio Canova's Visiting Card*
(By kind permission of the Dowager Countess of Cawdor)